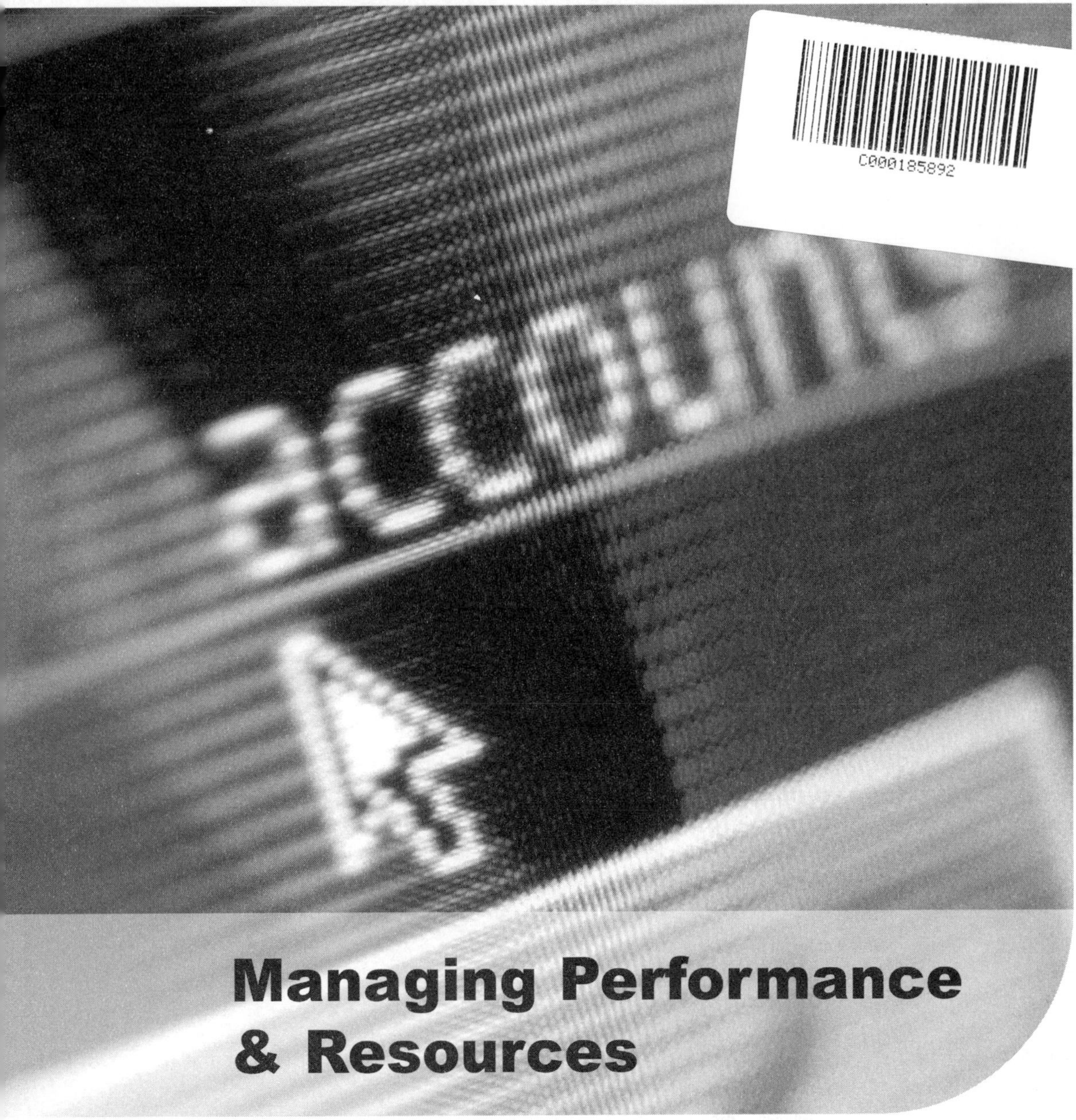

Managing Performance & Resources

Workbook

NVQ Accounting Units 8 & 9

Janet Brammer

Published by Osborne Books Limited
Unit 1B Everoak Estate
Bromyard Road
Worcester WR2 5HP
Tel 01905 748071
Email books@osbornebooks.co.uk
Website www.osbornebooks.co.uk

Design by Richard Holt
Cover image from Getty Images

Printed by the Bath Press, Bath

British Library Cataloguing in Publication Data
A catalogue record for this book is available from the British Library

ISBN 1 872962 67 X

Contents

Acknowledgements

The author wishes to thank the following for their help with the editing and production of the book: Mike Fardon, Mike Gilbert, Rosemarie Griffiths, Claire McCarthy, Jon Moore and Pineapple Publishing. Special thanks go to Roger Petheram, Series Editor, for reading, checking and advising on the development of this workbook.

The publisher is indebted to the Association of Accounting Technicians for its generous help and advice to our authors and editors during the preparation of this text, and for permission to reproduce extracts from the Standards of Competence for Accounting and sample assessment material.

Author

Janet Brammer has over twelve years' experience lecturing on AAT and ACCA accountancy courses at Norwich City College. She is a Certified Accountant and worked in accountancy practice for a number of years. She has also tutored for the Open University and has written a workbook *Management Information Framework* for the ACCA distance learning scheme. Janet is also co-author of *Active Accounting* and *Managing Performance & Resources Tutorial* from Osborne Books.

How to use this book

Managing Performance & Resources Workbook is designed to be used alongside Osborne Books' *Managing Performance & Resources Tutorial* and is ideal for student use in the classroom, at home and on distance learning courses. Both the Tutorial and the Workbook are designed for students preparing for assessment on the two core units in Management Accounting:

- Contributing to the management of performance and the enhancement of value
- Contributing to the planning and control of resources

Managing Performance & Resources Workbook is divided into three sections: Workbook Activities, Assignments and Practice Examination Tasks.

Workbook Activities

Workbook activities are self-contained exercises which are designed to be used to supplement the activities in the tutorial text. Many of them are more extended than the exercises in the tutorial and provide useful practice for students preparing for assessments. There are activities relating to each chapter of the tutorial text.

Assignments

The assignments in this section are more extended case study activities, similar to those which are used in Examinations. These are intended to be used as students progress through the course, to consolidate learning and to practise the application of methods and techniques. The required chapters of the tutorial text are therefore quoted at the beginning of each assignment and also on the assignment summary on page 77.

Practice Examinations

Osborne Books is grateful to the AAT for their kind permission for the reproduction of the AAT Specimen Examinations in this section and selected tasks from other Examinations. The remaining tasks are based on the kinds of tasks which have been used in Examinations on the two management accounting units.

answers

The answers to the tasks and exams in the *Workbook* are available in a separate *Tutor Pack*. Contact the Osborne Books Sales Office on 01905 748071 for details of how to obtain the Tutor Pack.

Workbook activities

This section contains activities which are suitable for use with the individual chapters of *Managing Performance & Resources Tutorial* from Osborne Books.

1 MANAGEMENT INFORMATION

1.1 All kinds of information, and management information in particular, must satisfy certain criteria in order to be useful.

List and explain briefly five criteria which should be satisfied by information if it is to be useful.

1.2 Fino Ltd provides a spray-painting service for manufacturers of various products. The work of Fino Ltd consists of three activities: preparation, painting and storage. The following budgeted information is available for Fino Ltd for the next year:

Activity	**Cost Driver**	**Budgeted Cost Pool**	**Budgeted Demand**
Preparation	Minutes	£375,000	750,000 minutes
Painting	Minutes	£960,000	384,000 minutes
Storage	Cubic metres	£510,000	255,000 cubic metres

Required:

(a) Calculate the cost driver rates for each of the three activities of Fino Ltd.

(b) Calculate the budgeted cost per unit of products X and Y, which require the following:

	X	**Y**
Preparation	8 minutes	12 minutes
Painting	10 minutes	6 minutes
Storage	0.25 cubic m	0.5 cubic m

1.3 Delta Ltd is an engineering firm which manufactures three products, A, B and C. Product C is produced in smaller quantities for one specific customer. The following planned and budgeted information is available for the coming year:

Overheads:	£
Production set-up costs	246,000
Raw materials inwards department	66,300
Raw materials stores	99,000
Total	411,300

Product:	*A*	*B*	*C*
Budgeted production (units)	40,000	30,000	15,000
Batch size (units)	2,500	3,000	1,000
Direct material cost per unit	£25	£30	£16
Direct labour cost per unit	£4	£2	£1
Direct labour hours per unit	0.5	0.25	0.125
Expected number of raw materials deliveries in year	10	6	10
Expected number of materials requisitions	16	20	30

Required: giving your answers in £ correct to 2 decimal places:

(a) Calculate a single overhead absorption rate for the total overheads of £411,300 on a direct labour hour basis. (Hint: you will first need to calculate the total labour hours required for the budgeted production of the products.)

(b) Calculate the direct cost per unit and the total cost per unit of each of the products A, B and C, using absorption costing. Use your answer to (a) to calculate the absorbed overheads.

(c) In order to apply the Activity Based Costing method to Delta Ltd, a cost driver rate must be calculated for each activity using:

$$\textit{Cost driver rate} = \frac{\textit{Budgeted cost pool}}{\textit{Total budgeted demand for cost driver}}$$

Using this method, calculate the cost driver rates to be charged for the three activities as follows:

- Production set-up costs to be charged on the basis of number of batches.
- Raw materials inwards to be charged on the basis of number of deliveries.
- Raw materials stores to be charged on the basis of number of requisitions.

(d) Using your answers to (c) and Activity Based Costing, calculate the overheads to be included in the total cost of production for each of the products A, B and C.

(e) Using your answers to (d), calculate the total cost per unit of each of the products A, B and C, using Activity Based Costing. Show the direct cost as a subtotal before adding the overheads in each case.

1.4 Abmar Ltd manufactures one product of the same name, the Abmar. The variable costs of producing 10,000 Abmars during the year ended 30 June 2004 were:

Direct Materials	£70,000
Direct Labour	£40,000
Variable Production Overheads	£30,000

The fixed costs incurred by Abmar Ltd in the year ended 30 June 2004 were:

Fixed production overheads	£50,000
Other fixed overheads	£60,000

The selling price was £30 per Abmar.

Of the 10,000 Abmars produced, only 8,000 were sold during the year.

The opening stock of finished Abmars was zero and there was no opening or closing work-in-progress.

Required:

(a) Calculate the cost of one Abmar using Marginal Costing.

(b) Set out a marginal costing statement for Abmar Ltd for the year ended 30 June 2004, showing the contribution (in total) and the total reported profit.

(c) Given that Fixed Production Overheads are to be absorbed on a per unit basis, but Other Fixed Overheads are not absorbed, calculate the absorption cost of one Abmar.

(d) Set out an absorption costing statement for Abmar Ltd for the year ended 30 June 2004, showing the total reported profit.

(e) Calculate the difference in reported profit between your answer in (b) and your answer in (d). What is the reason for this difference?

1.5 The standard cost per unit of a product is as follows:

		£
Direct Materials: 5kg at £5 per kg		25
Direct Labour: 5hrs at £8 per hour		40
Variable production overhead:		
	5hrs at £3 per direct labour hour	15
Fixed production overhead:		
	5hrs at £4 per direct labour hour	20

Budgeted production totals 1,500 units of the product in a given period.

There are other fixed overheads of £50,000 in total for the period.

The selling price of the product is £170 per unit.

Required:

For each of the following two periods, prepare marginal costing and absorption costing operating statements for this product. In each case, reconcile the reported profit figures for the two costing methods.

(a) In a given period, 1,500 units of the product are made, but only 1,200 are sold. There is no opening stock of finished goods.

(b) In the next period, with an opening stock of 300 units, 1,000 units are made and 1,200 are sold.

1.6 Arnold Ltd makes a single product, the Arno. On completion of production, 2% of the Arnos are found to be faulty and have to be scrapped. Production workers work independently of each other in making Arnos, and the production manager wants to establish whether certain workers are responsible for most of the faulty Arnos.

Required:

(a) Identify two advantages of sampling for establishing the reasons for the faulty Arnos.

(b) Explain briefly what is meant by

- true (or simple) random sampling
- systematic sampling
- stratified sampling

(c) State which form of sampling would be most appropriate for Arnold Ltd.

1.7 A moving average trend in Sales Volume has been calculated as follows:

Time period:	3	4	5	6	7	8
Moving average trend (000s units)	931.0	942.4	953.3	964.6	975.7	987.0

Required:

(a) Calculate the average change in the trend per period.

(b) Forecast the trend in sales volume for each of the time periods 9, 10, 11 and 12, assuming the trend continues.

1.8 (a) Calculate a *three-point* moving average trend for the data:

902 890 940 900 905 950

(b) Calculate a *five-point* moving average trend for the data:

74 77 70 75 80 79 82 74 85 90

1.9 Toto Toys has the following quarterly turnover figures for the three years starting 1 July 2004.

Toto Toys: Turnover in £000s

	Quarter 1	*Quarter 2*	*Quarter 3*	*Quarter 4*
2004			482	560
2005	493	528	520	604
2006	530	571	558	642
2007	570	609		

Required:

(a) Set out the Toto Toys turnover data in a column and calculate a centred four-point moving average trend.

(b) Using your answer to (a), calculate average additive (absolute) seasonal variations in turnover.

(c) Assuming that the trend and the pattern of additive seasonal variations continue, calculate forecast turnover figures for Toto Toys for each of quarters 3 and 4 of 2007.

1.10 Spring Ltd sells a range of outdoor clothing, including lightweight showerproof jackets, for which the quarterly sales volumes over a period of three years are shown below.

	Quarter 1	*Quarter 2*	*Quarter 3*	*Quarter 4*
2003	2,530	2,700	2,610	2,480
2004	2,730	2,940	2,850	2,620
2005	2,950	3,100	3,050	2,820

Required:

(a) Set out the Spring Ltd data in a column and calculate centred four-point moving average sales volumes for the showerproof jackets. (Use 1 decimal place in workings.)

(b) Using your answer to (a), calculate average *percentage* seasonal variations (to the nearest whole number) in the sales of Spring Ltd's showerproof jackets.

(c) Assuming that the trend and the pattern of percentage seasonal variations will continue, forecast the sales volume of Spring Ltd's showerproof jackets for each of the four quarters of 2006.

1.11 An assistant management accountant in Snap Ltd is testing computer software for the analysis of trends and seasonal variations. After inputting several years' historical sales data relating to Snap Ltd's photographic film, the following output has been obtained:

Analysis of sales of photographic film (sales volume in numbers of films)

Regression line trend: $y = 8{,}000x + 150{,}000$

This may be written: Trend value = (8,000 x Quarter Number) + 150,000

	Seasonal Variations	
Quarter of the year	*Absolute*	*Percentage*
First	–100,000	–30%
Second	+50,000	+15%
Third	+170,000	+60%
Fourth	–120,000	–45%

Actual numbers of films sold in quarters 17 to 20 are shown below. Quarter 17 was a 'first' quarter of a year, quarter 18 a 'second' quarter, and so on.

Quarter	*Number of films sold*
17	185,000
18	345,500
19	471,600
20	189,000

Required:

(a) Using the regression line formula, calculate the trend for the sales of films in quarters 17, 18, 19 and 20.

(b) Using your answer to (a) and the absolute seasonal variations, calculate the resulting forecasts for the film sales in quarters 17 to 20 inclusive.

(c) Using your answer to (a) and the percentage seasonal variations, calculate the resulting forecasts for the film sales in quarters 17 to 20 inclusive.

(d) By comparing the two sets of forecasts with the actual film sales given for quarters 17 to 20, identify which method of calculating the seasonal variations gives the best estimates of actual sales of films.

(e) Using the method which you have identified as best in (d), calculate the forecast sales numbers of films for Snap Ltd for Quarters 21 to 24 inclusive.

1.12 **Required:** answer the following questions using index numbers:

(a) In the base year of a suitable price index (ie when the index number was 100), product P cost £3. The price index is now 130. What would the cost of product P be in today's terms?

(b) The market value of a house at the present time is £180,000. A suitable index for house prices is now at a level of 145. What would the price of this house be in terms of the prices 5 years ago, when this house price index was 116?

(c) A group of workers has been awarded a 2% wage increase for the next year. If the retail prices index goes up from 124 to 128 for the next year, are the workers better or worse off in real terms?

(d) Average salaries for staff in the head office of a company over 5 years are given below, together with an index of general prices for the same years.

Year	***Average Salary***	***Price Index***
1	£16,000	120
2	£16,300	122
3	£16,700	123
4	£17,000	126
5	£17,200	128

- Calculate the average salaries for each of the five years in terms of Year 5 prices. Give your answers to the nearest £.
- Comment on the results of your calculations.

(e) The price of a material is currently £24.00 per kg and a suitable price index is 120. The index is forecast to rise to 125 in a year's time. What would be the forecast price of the material at that time?

After a year, it was found that the index actually rose to 122. Calculate the error in the forecast of the material price.

2 STANDARD COSTING – DIRECT COSTS

2.1 (a) The standard cost per unit of product A includes:

Direct Material: 2 kg at £5.50 per kg.

In a given period, 10,500 units of product A were made, using 20,000 kg of Direct Material, at a total cost of £98,000.

Required:

Calculate the Direct Material Price and Usage Variances for Product A for this period.

(b) The standard cost budget for 1,500 units of product B includes 4,500 metres of Direct Material at a total cost of £5,400.

In a given period, 1,700 units of product B were made, using 5,400 metres of Direct Material, at a total cost of £8,000.

Required:

Calculate the Direct Material Price and Usage Variances for Product B for this period.

2.2 (a) The standard cost per unit of product A includes:

Direct Labour: 0.5 hours at £6 per hour.

In a given period, 10,500 units of product A were made, taking 5,700 Direct Labour hours, at a total cost of £35,000.

Required:

Calculate the Direct Labour Rate and Efficiency Variances for Product A for this period.

(b) The standard cost budget for 1,500 units of product B includes 3,000 hours of Direct Labour at a total cost of £24,000.

In a given period, 1,700 units of product B were made, taking 3,500 Direct Labour hours, at a total cost of £26,000.

Required:

Calculate the Direct Labour Rate and Efficiency Variances For Product B for this period.

2.3 The standard cost per unit of product C includes the following direct costs:

Direct Material: 1.5 kg at £16 per kg = £24 per product unit

Direct Labour: 4 hours at £7 per hour = £28 per product unit

In a given period, the actual results were as follows:

6,300 units of product C were made

10,000 kg of Direct Material were used, total cost £165,400

Direct Labour cost £180,000 for 25,200 hours

Required: for Product C for this period:

(a) calculate the Direct Material Price and Usage Variances for this period.

(b) calculate the Direct Labour Rate and Efficiency Variances for this period.

(c) suggest possible reasons for the direct cost variances in this period.

2.4 State whether each of the following statements is true or false.

(a) Normal amounts of wastage of direct materials are allowed for when the standard cost of a product is set.

(b) If more product units are produced than planned, the direct materials usage variance will be adverse.

(c) If the direct labour (total) variance is adverse, it means that the labour force worked more slowly than the standard.

(d) Direct materials usage variances are based on the standard prices of the materials.

(e) If forecasts under-estimate the rate of inflation when standards are set, all the direct cost variances will be adverse.

(f) Purchasing a substitute for the normal direct material can affect both the price and usage variances.

2.5 The standard cost per unit of a product includes:

Direct material: 2.5 kg at £9.00 per kg

Direct Labour: 20 minutes at £6.00 per hour.

In a given period, the actual results were as follows:

7,620 product units were manufactured.

Direct material cost £8.80 per kg and 20,000 kg were used.

Direct labour rate was £6.60 per hour and the total cost was £16,500.

Required:

(a) Calculate the direct material price and usage variances for the given period.

(b) Calculate the direct labour rate and efficiency variances for the given period.

(c) Set out a reconciliation of the standard direct cost of the actual output with the total actual direct cost, showing the variances calculated in (a) and (b).

2.6 Varan Ltd has the following budgeted and actual direct cost and production data for its single product for the last three months.

	Budget	*Budget*	*Actual*	*Actual*
Production units	12,000		12,300	
Direct materials	36,000 m	£223,200	37,000 m	£250,000
Direct labour	24,000 hrs	£115,200	25,000 hrs	£122,500
Total direct costs		£338,400		£372,500

Required: Calculate all the direct cost variances for Varan Ltd for the last three month period and use them to reconcile the standard direct cost for the actual production level with the actual costs.

2.7 Margan Ltd uses marginal costing and has the following budgeted and actual variable cost and production data for the month of November.

	Budget	*Budget*	*Actual*	*Actual*
Production units	8,500		8,200	
Variable materials	10,625 kg	£63,750	10,100 kg	£63,630
Variable labour:				
Grade I	4,250 hrs	£35,700	4,000 hrs	£34,000
Grade II	6,375 hrs	£51,000	6,300 hrs	£50,400
Total variable costs		£150,450		£148,030

Required: Calculate all the relevant variable cost variances (keeping Grade I and II labour separate) and use them to reconcile the standard marginal cost for the actual production level with the actual marginal cost.

2.8 Rust Ltd manufactures a single product, the Rek. The standard direct costs of one Rek are as follows:

Direct Material: 4 kg @ £0.80 per kg =	£3.20
Direct Labour: 1.5 hours @ £8.00 per hour =	£12.00
Total direct cost	£15.20

In October 2004, Rust Ltd produced 9,000 Reks, and the total actual direct costs of production were £30,000 for direct material and £105,000 for direct labour.

The direct material usage variance for October 2004 has been calculated as £800 Favourable, and the Direct Labour Efficiency Variance as £4,000 Adverse.

Required:

(a) Calculate the total standard direct cost of production for 9,000 Reks.

(b) Calculate the total actual cost of production for October 2004.

(c) Calculate the direct material (total) variance for October 2004 and hence calculate the direct material price variance.

(d) Calculate the direct labour (total) variance for October 2004 and hence calculate the direct labour rate variance.

(e) Prepare a direct cost reconciliation statement for Rust Ltd for October 2004, showing the total standard and actual costs and all the variances.

(f) Eight possible separate causes of variances are given below. For each one, state whether it appears to be a valid reason for the variances shown in (e), and if so, to which variances it may have contributed.

1 Production was interrupted due to a machine breakdown.

2 The supplier has improved the specification of the material.

3 An employee's mistake caused materials to be wasted.

4 There was a national wage increase, applicable to Rust Ltd's employees, which came into force on 1 October 2004.

5 The direct workers included a considerable number of trainees, who started work this month.

6 A bonus was offered to direct workers to encourage greater efficiency.

7 The purchasing department ordered the material from a different supplier.

8 The employees were deliberately working slowly in October to highlight their claim for a pay increase.

2.9 Garth Ltd uses standard costing in the preparation of its budgets. The following information relates to the budgeted and actual results for a given year for product Zed, which is one of the products manufactured by Garth Ltd.

Budget information: Product Zed

Production volume	1,200 units of Zed
Direct material quantity	7,200 kg
Total cost of direct material	£36,000
Direct labour hours	8,400 hours
Total direct labour cost	£50,400

Actual results : Product Zed

Production volume	1,400 units of Zed
Direct material quantity	8,200 kg
Total cost of direct material	£42,640
Direct labour hours	9,400 hours
Total direct labour cost	£56,500

During this period, a customer put in an extra order for Product Zed at short notice, which meant that a batch of direct material had to be purchased from a local supplier. This material was slightly different from that normally used in Product Zed, and was more expensive. Some overtime was worked to complete the order on time and the premium paid to employees for this was included in the direct labour cost.

Required:

(a) Calculate all the direct material and direct labour variances for Product Zed for the given year.

(b) Prepare a statement reconciling the standard direct cost of actual output with the actual direct cost of Product Zed for the given year.

(c) Write a Memo to the manager of Garth Ltd, suggesting reasons for the difference between the standard and actual costs.

3 STANDARD COSTING – FIXED OVERHEADS

3.1 The budget for product A for a given period includes £48,000 of fixed overheads, to be absorbed on direct labour hours at a rate of £8 per direct labour hour. The planned production of product A is 12,000 units, the standard direct labour hours being 0.5 hours per unit of product A.

The actual results for the period were as follows:

10,500 units of product A were made, taking 5,700 direct labour hours.
Total actual fixed overheads amounted to £50,000.

Required:

Calculate for product A for the given period:

- the total fixed overhead variance
- the fixed overhead expenditure variance
- the fixed overhead volume variance
- the fixed overhead capacity variance
- the fixed overhead efficiency variance

3.2 The planned production of product B for a given period is 1,500 units. The standard cost per unit of B includes fixed overheads absorbed at a rate of £30 per direct labour hour. Each unit of B should take 2 hours of direct labour according to the standard.

In the given period, 1,700 units of product B were actually made, taking 3,500 direct labour hours. The actual fixed overheads were £85,000.

Required:

Calculate for product B for the given period:

- the total fixed overhead variance
- the fixed overhead expenditure variance
- the fixed overhead volume variance
- the fixed overhead capacity variance
- the fixed overhead efficiency variance

3.3 Margan Ltd uses marginal costing and has the following budgeted and actual fixed cost data for the month of November.

	Budget	*Actual*
Production units	8,500	8,200
Fixed costs	£90,100	£85,000

Required:

(a) Calculate the fixed cost (expenditure) variance for Margan Ltd for November.

(b) Explain briefly why there is no further analysis of fixed cost variances when marginal costing is being used.

3.4 The standard direct labour time per unit of a product is 20 minutes. Fixed overheads are to be absorbed on direct labour hours at an overhead absorption rate of £12.60 per hour, based on budgeted production of 7,800 units.

In a given period, the actual results were as follows:

7,620 product units were manufactured.

Direct labour hours used were 2,500 hours.

Actual fixed production overhead amounted to £33,000.

Required:

(a) Calculate the following fixed overhead variances for this product for the given period:

- total fixed overhead variance
- fixed overhead expenditure variance
- fixed overhead capacity variance
- fixed overhead efficiency variance
- fixed overhead volume variance

(b) Which of the following statements is true for this case?

1 Production output was more than planned, resulting in a favourable efficiency variance.

2 Direct labour hours were less than planned, resulting in an adverse capacity variance.

3 Fixed overheads were over-absorbed.

4 Output was produced using less hours than the standard for the actual number of units.

5 Spending on fixed overheads was less than expected.

3.5 Varan Ltd has the following budgeted and actual direct cost and production data for its single product for the last three months.

	Budget	*Budget*	*Actual*	*Actual*
Production units	12,000		12,300	
Direct materials	36,000 m	£223,200	37,000 m	£250,000
Direct labour	24,000 hrs	£115,200	25,000 hrs	£122,500
Fixed production overhead		£14,400		£16,000
Machine hours	18,000 hrs		18,500 hrs	

Required:

(a) Calculate the fixed production overhead absorption rate for Varan Ltd, based on machine hours.

(b) Calculate the budgeted amount of fixed production overhead per unit of the product, using your answer to (a).

(c) Calculate all the direct cost variances for Varan Ltd for the last three month period. (You may have already calculated these in Activity 2.6.)

(d) Calculate all the fixed overhead variances for Varan Ltd for the last three month period.

(e) Prepare a reconciliation statement for Varan Ltd's actual output for the last three months, showing the total standard and actual costs and all the variances calculated in (c) and (d) above.

(f) Seven possible separate causes of variances are given below. For each one, state whether it appears to be a valid reason for the variances shown in (e), and if so, to which variances it may have contributed.

1. A customer increased his order for the product at short notice.
2. Due to extra demand for the product, insufficient direct materials were in stock, and a slightly different substitute material had to be obtained at short notice from a different supplier.
3. Production was interrupted due to a machine breakdown.
4. There was a national wage increase, applicable to Varan Ltd's employees, which came into force during this period.
5. A number of production staff were off sick and therefore additional overtime was worked by others.
6. A bonus was offered to direct workers to encourage greater efficiency.
7. There have been improvements in production methods since the standard was set.

3.6 Island Holidays Ltd specialises in arranging holidays to a small island. The company uses its own 105-seat aircraft to transfer tourists to and from the island. The following report was presented to the manager of Island Holidays Ltd:

Island Holidays Ltd Operating Statement for Quarter 3, 2004

	Budget	*Actual*
Number of holidays	6,000	7,800
	£	£
Turnover	1,800,000	2,262,000
Accommodation	840,000	1,048,944
Air transport	720,000	792,000
Operating profit	240,000	421,056

The manager considers this report unhelpful and requests a standard costing report, reconciling the standard and actual costs for the actual holidays sold in the quarter. You are given the following additional information:

The accommodation cost is a variable cost and the usage variance is zero.

Air transport is a fixed cost.

The budget for a volume of 6,000 holidays was based on air transport capacity of 80 return flights in the quarter, with an average of 75 tourists per flight. These standards were used to calculate the fixed overhead absorption rate when costing individual holidays.

Due to weather conditions, there were only 78 flights in this quarter, carrying a total of 7,800 tourists.

Required:

(a) Using the budgeted data, calculate the standard absorption cost per holiday

(b) Using your answer to (a), calculate the standard absorption cost of 7,800 holidays

(c) Calculate the following variances:

- material price variance for accommodation
- fixed overhead expenditure variance for air transport
- fixed overhead volume variance for air transport
- fixed overhead capacity variance for air transport
- fixed overhead efficiency variance for air transport

(d) Prepare a statement reconciling the standard absorption cost of 7,800 holidays to the actual total cost of 7,800 holidays

(e) Calculate the actual total cost per holiday and identify the most important reason why this was lower than the standard absorption cost per holiday.

3.7 Image Dry Cleaners run four shops, each of which is equipped with a dry cleaning machine. Whenever possible, each machine is run with a full load, which is on average 20 items. The shops are open six days a week, and each machine can be used to dry clean a maximum of 5 loads per day, but Image's budget is set on the basis of 4 loads per machine per weekday, and 2 loads per machine on Saturdays. Image Dry Cleaners' budgeted fixed overheads are £6,160 per week and are absorbed on a machine run basis, with the standard set at an average load of 15 items per machine run.

During the week commencing 10 September 2004, the actual fixed overheads amounted to £6,010. Results from the Image shops showed:

	Number of machine runs	*Items cleaned*
North shop	18	288
South shop	24	384
East shop	20	300
West shop	20	288
Total	82	1,260

Required:

(a) Identify the output of Image Dry Cleaners and how it is measured in standard form. Calculate the fixed overhead absorption rate per machine run.

(b) Calculate all the fixed overhead variances for Image Dry Cleaners for the week commencing 10 September 2004.

(c) Write a short report to the manager of Image Dry Cleaners, summarising the subdivision of the fixed overhead variance into expenditure, volume, capacity and efficiency variances. Include brief comments on the meaning of these variances in relation to the actual results and the usefulness of the analysis.

3.8 The Village Museum is a small private museum, which is open each day except Monday, throughout the year. The costs of running the museum are all costs which relate to time periods and do not depend on the number of visitors. Visitors are charged for entry and can stay as long as they wish in the museum on that day. The fixed costs for the first six months of the current year were budgeted as £8,400 and the total number of visitors expected was 2,400.

The actual fixed costs for the first six months of the current year were £8,670 and the actual total number of visitors was 2,550.

Required:

(a) Calculate a fixed cost absorption rate for the museum, based on the number of visitors.

(b) Calculate the fixed cost variance for the first six months of the current year, and analyse it into expenditure and volume variances. State why each of these variances has arisen.

(c) Explain briefly why analysis of the volume variance into capacity and efficiency variances would not be relevant in this case.

3.9 The Riviera Swimming Pool is open for 1,200 hours per quarter. There should be five staff on duty throughout opening hours. The cost budget for the second quarter of 2004 is shown below, together with the actual costs for the quarter.

Riviera Swimming Pool: Quarter 2, 2004

	Budget	*Actual*
Opening hours	1,200	1,200
Direct material for water treatment: quantity (litres)	4,500	4,620
Direct material cost (£)	8,100	8,300
Direct labour hours	6,000	5,900
Direct labour cost (£)	32,400	32,450
Fixed overheads (£)	28,000	30,000
Number of customer visits	20,000	18,600

Required:

(a) Calculate:

- the standard cost per litre of direct material
- the standard cost per direct labour hour
- the fixed overhead absorption rate, based on the number of customer visits

(b) Calculate, for quarter 2, 2004:

- the direct material price variance
- the direct labour rate variance
- the fixed overhead expenditure variance
- the fixed overhead volume variance, based on the budgeted and actual numbers of customer visits

(c) Explain briefly why it is not appropriate to split the fixed overhead volume variance into capacity and efficiency variances in this case.

4 STANDARD COSTING – FURTHER ANALYSIS

4.1 (a) Explain briefly the meaning and implications of each of the following, in relation to standard costing:

- ideal standard
- attainable standard
- basic standard

Which of these is most appropriate for the purposes of variance analysis and why?

(b) Explain briefly what is meant by the following terms in relation to variance analysis:

- control limits
- management by exception

(c) Give one example of how methods of costing and the setting of standards may affect the behaviour of a manager who is held responsible for particular variances.

4.2 The standard cost per litre of a material is £3.20, based on its expected average price over the coming year. Time series analysis of the cost of this item over the last 5 years indicates that the following additive seasonal variations in the price can be expected.

Quarter		
Quarter 1	January to March	– £0.10
2	April to June	+ £0.05
3	July to September	+ £0.10
4	October to December	– £0.05

Required:

Using the given data for each of the following months, calculate the Material Price Variance for this material, and analyse it into the part expected to be due to the seasonality of the price and the part due to other influences.

(a) In January, 18,000 litres were used, at a total cost of £54,000.

(b) In May, 18,000 litres were used, at a total cost of £58,140.

4.3 The standard cost per metre of a material is £20, based on its expected average price over the coming year. Time series analysis of the cost of this item over the last 5 years indicates that the following proportional (multiplicative) seasonal variations in the price can be expected.

Quarter		
Quarter 1	January to March	+15%
2	April to June	+5%
3	July to September	– 20%
4	October to December	zero

Required:

Using the given data for each of the following months, calculate the Material Price Variance for this material, and analyse it into the part expected to be due to the seasonality of the price and the part due to other influences.

(a) In May, 6,400 metres were used, at a total cost of £124,800.

(b) In September, 7,000 metres were used, at a total cost of £105,000.

4.4 A business set its standard price for a certain material when the appropriate price index was 148. The assumption was made that the index would rise to 150 by the time the standard was in use, and therefore the standard decided upon was £60 per unit of material, to take this into account. By the time the standard was in use, the index had actually risen to 152 and in a given month 5,800 units of material actually cost £350,900.

Required:

Calculate the Material Price Variance for this material, and analyse it into the part due to the actual change in the price index and the part due to other factors.

4.5 When standards were being decided upon, the appropriate wage rate index was expected to rise from 180 to 189, and the standard wage rate was set as £7.35 per hour to take account of this. In fact, by the time the standard was in use, an increase of 4% had been brought in for the relevant employees. In a given period, £79,056 was paid for a total of 10,800 hours.

Required:

Calculate the Labour Rate Variance for this period, and analyse it into the part due to the actual pay award and the part due to other factors.

4.6 A company imports a direct material from Beta Island and pays in Beta Dollars (B$). The standard price per unit of the material was set in B$, equivalent to £36, when the exchange rate was B$5 to the £. The exchange rate is subject to fluctuations, however, due to instability in the Beta Island economy.

Required:

For each of the following months, calculate the Material Price Variance, and analyse it into the part due to exchange rate changes and the part due to other factors.

(a) In June the exchange rate was B$4.50 = £1. In June 7,500 units of material cost £307,500 in total.

(b) In September the exchange rate was B$6 = £1. In September 8,000 units of material cost £256,000 in total.

4.7 A company imports a direct material from Gamma Island and pays in Gamma Dollars (G$). The standard price per unit of the material was set in G$, equivalent to £40, when the exchange rate was G$30 to the £. The exchange rate is subject to fluctuations, however, due to instability in the Gamma Island economy.

Required:

For each of the following months, calculate the Material Price Variance, and analyse it into the part due to exchange rate changes and the part due to other factors.

(a) In July the exchange rate was G$32 = £1. In July 4,800 units of material cost £168,000 in total.

(b) In November the exchange rate was G$25 = £1. In November 5,200 units of material cost £260,000 in total.

4.8 The standard cost per unit of product UV includes:

Direct material: 4 kg at £2.50 per kg, ie £10.00 per unit of UV

Direct Labour: 1.5 hours at £6.20 per hour, ie £9.30 per unit of UV

In a given period, the actual results were that 4,500 units of UV were produced, using 20,000 kg of direct material and taking 6,400 direct labour hours. The total cost of direct material was £48,000 and the total cost of direct labour was £40,000.

Required: for Product UV for the given period:

(a) calculate the direct material total variance and split it into price and usage variances.

(b) calculate the direct labour total variance and split it into rate and efficiency variances.

(c) After calculating the variances as above, additional information becomes available:

The standard for direct material usage should have been changed to 4.2 kg per unit of UV for this period, due to a change in its specification.

The standard for direct labour time was set at 90% level of efficiency for a previous period, when staff were being trained. For the given period, 100% level of efficiency was expected and the standard had not been updated.

(i) Calculate the part of the direct material usage variance due to the incorrect standard and the part due to other reasons.

(ii) Calculate the part of the direct labour efficiency variance due to the out of date level of efficiency in the standard and the part due to other reasons.

4.9 The standard cost per unit of product W includes:

Direct material: 7 kg at £8.00 per kg, ie £56.00 per unit of W

Direct Labour: 4 hours at £5.00 per hour, ie £20.00 per unit of W

In a given period, the actual results were that 16,000 units of W were produced, using 113,600 kg of direct material and taking 68,640 direct labour hours. The total cost of direct material was £920,160 and the total cost of direct labour was £336,336.

Required: for Product W for the given period:

(a) calculate the direct material total variance and split it into price and usage variances.

(b) calculate the direct labour total variance and split it into rate and efficiency variances.

(c) After calculating the variances as above, additional information becomes available:

The standard for the price of direct material should have been increased by 1.25% for this period, due to a change in supplier.

Production workers are new to this work and are currently taking 10% longer to make a unit of W than they will when fully trained.

(i) Calculate the part of the direct material price variance due to the incorrect standard and the part due to other reasons.

(ii) Calculate the part of the direct labour efficiency variance due to the production workers not yet being fully trained and the part due to other reasons.

4.10 Brighter Chemicals makes a single product, XZ, which is sold in 5-litre tins. Fixed overheads are absorbed on the basis of direct labour hours. Budgeted production is 1,750 tins per month and the standard cost per tin is as follows:

Direct material: 5 litres at £40 per litre =	£200 per tin of XZ
Direct labour: 10 hours at £6 per hour =	£60 per tin of XZ
Fixed overheads: 10 hours at £24 per hour =	£240 per tin of XZ

During the month of May 2004, actual production was 1,700 tins of XZ and the actual total costs were as follows:

Direct material	£338,283
Direct labour	£110,330
Fixed overheads	£410,000

The actual cost of direct material was £40.20 per litre and the actual direct labour rate was £5.90 per hour.

Required:

(a) Calculate for the month of May 2004:

(i) actual litres of material used

(ii) actual hours worked

(iii) standard quantity of material for the actual output of 1,700 tins of XZ

(iv) standard direct labour hours for the actual output of 1,700 tins of XZ

(v) the total budgeted fixed overheads

(b) Calculate the following variances for the month of May 2004:

(i) direct material price variance

(ii) direct material usage variance

(iii) direct labour rate variance

(iv) direct labour efficiency variance

(v) fixed overhead expenditure variance

(vi) fixed overhead volume variance

(vii) fixed overhead capacity variance

(viii) fixed overhead efficiency variance

(c) Prepare a statement for the month of May 2004, reconciling the standard cost of the actual output of XZ to the actual cost, detailing the variances

(d) You are given the following additional information after preparing the statement in part (c):

- the direct material used is purchased in drums, each of which has a guaranteed minimum content
- the tins of output of XZ are filled by a machine and the amounts put into the tins may vary very slightly
- an appropriate index of raw material prices was 124.00 when the direct material standard price was set, but by May 2004 it was actually 125.86

You are asked to write a short memo to the production director, explaining:

(i) three factors which may have contributed to the favourable direct material usage variance, but which do not represent efficient usage of the material

(ii) why it is important to investigate favourable variances as well as adverse variances

(iii) how the material price variance has arisen partly due to the change in the standard cost as measured by the material price index and partly due to other reasons, showing your calculation of these two parts.

5 MEASURING QUALITY

5.1 The managers of a large department store wish to review the quality of the *service* (not the products) provided to customers in the various store departments. They have decided to carry out a survey, by asking customers to complete a short questionnaire.

Required:

(a) Suggest four aspects of the service that should be covered by the questionnaire.

(b) For each of the four categories listed below, give an example of a cost of quality of the service offered by the department store.

- Prevention costs
- Appraisal costs
- Internal failure costs
- External failure costs

5.2 (a) Explain briefly the implications and the benefits of implementing a policy of Total Quality Management in an organisation.

(b) Suggest how an organisation with a policy of Total Quality Management may tackle the following problems:

- A large number of complaints from customers that they are unable to get through on the telephone when they wish to place an order.
- Several cases of materials being wasted due to machine failure.

5.3 Smith's Wheels make wheels for model trains. The wheels are made by automatic machining and then assembled in pairs on axles. The wheels are sold to individual model-makers, model railway clubs, shops and to toy manufacturers to incorporate in their model trains. Accurate machining and assembly of the wheels and axles is essential for the trains to work.

After the machining process 2% of the wheels are scrapped because they are faulty. It is estimated that, after assembly, 4% of the finished products are substandard and Smith's inspection identifies three-quarters of these, which are also scrapped.

Smith's Wheels guarantee to replace any faulty wheels returned by customers.

The variable cost of making each wheel is £0.20 and the cost of the axle and assembly for each pair is £0.15, so that the variable cost of the finished product is £0.55.

In a given period, Smith's Wheels commence production with machining 40,000 wheels. Assume that all finished production which passes inspection is sold, and all faulty wheels sold are returned.

Required: for the given period:

(a) Calculate the number of wheels scrapped after machining.

(b) Calculate the number of substandard assembled pairs of wheels, and the quantity of these which are scrapped. How many substandard products are therefore sold?

(c) Calculate the costs of quality associated with your answers to (a) and (b) above.

(d) Identify two further costs of quality for Smith's Wheels which are not included in your calculations.

5.4 White Ltd runs a linen supply service for a number of hotels in a large city. Clean towels, sheets etc, supplied from White Ltd's own stock, are delivered to each hotel on a daily basis. Used linen is collected and laundered in White Ltd's own laundry.

Problems arise with the hotels if delivery is delayed, if the standard of cleanliness or the condition of items is unsatisfactory, or if the numbers of items supplied is incorrect. There have recently been a number of complaints from hotel managers about the service offered by White Ltd.

The managing director of White Ltd held a meeting with staff representatives from all departments, whose comments included the following:

- The laundry has recently started using cheaper washing liquid.
- The delivery vans have broken down three times in three months.
- The requirements from the hotels come in by telephone. The calls are often made by a junior employee at the hotel and may contain mistakes. A junior White Ltd employee may take the calls.
- Delivery routes have not been reviewed for over a year, during which time several new hotels have been added and some new road traffic schemes have been introduced in the city.
- Some of the equipment in the laundry is out-dated and inefficient.
- Packing staff do not have sufficient time to inspect the items thoroughly or to double check the count of items in the bags.

Required: for White Ltd's linen supply service:

(a) Identify the features of the service which represent its value to the customer.

(b) Suggest ways in which the problems identified at the meeting may be addressed, and the associated effects on costs of quality which would arise in each case.

5.5 Pix Ltd manufactures cameras, and has recently carried out an investigation into the reliability of one of its relatively new products, a digital camera. Investigations show that 1 in every 1,500 of these cameras quickly develops a fault and ceases to work. It is estimated that 80% of these are returned to Pix Ltd. A repair which costs the company £30 corrects the fault.

A further 2 in every 1,500 of these cameras are returned to Pix Ltd because they are considered by customers to produce unsatisfactory results. Pix Ltd gives these customers full refunds, and after checking the cameras at a cost of £10, sells them as 'reconditioned' at a discount of £100 on the usual selling price.

It is estimated that the costs of advertising in order to replace customers who were dissatisfied with Pix Ltd's digital cameras amount to £60,000 per year. Average sales of these digital cameras are currently 75,000 per year, but Pix Ltd's managers had anticipated significant sales growth in the coming year.

Required:

List the explicit costs of quality in this case, stating the category of each and the amount where possible.

Identify an example of an implicit cost of quality in this case.

5.6 (a) From your own point of view as a consumer, suggest the features which give a camera its value.

(b) From the point of view of a camera manufacturer, list four questions which may be asked in carrying out a value analysis of their products.

5.7 **Required:**

(a) Give two reasons why it is important to plan long-term cost reduction policies, rather than introduce crash programmes for cutting costs.

(b) Suggest two ways in which work study may help to reduce costs in a factory.

(c) List three ways in which a manufacturing company may reduce costs, other than on production.

(d) 'Value engineering' may be applied to a new product being developed. What are the main implications this would have for the design of the product?

(e) Explain briefly what is meant by the statement 'variety reduction can reduce costs and enhance value'.

5.8 Gill Ltd make a single product, the Gamma, each unit of which uses a component G3. Purchases of G3 are all inspected on receipt and some are found to be faulty. These are returned to the supplier, but further units of G3 develop faults when used in the product Gamma. As a result, costs are incurred in reworking production and in dealing with complaints in customer services.

In the following operating statement for Gill Ltd, marginal costing is used. Gill Ltd keeps no stocks of materials other than G3, nor of finished Gammas.

Gill Ltd: Operating Statement for the year ended 31 December 2004

	£000s	£000s
Turnover		1,800
Purchases of G3	350	
Less: returns of G3	(30)	
	320	
Add: opening stock	40	
Less: closing stock	(20)	
G3 issued to production	340	
Other variable costs	400	740
Contribution		1,060
Fixed production overhead	810	
G3 inspection costs	22	
Costs relating to purchases returns	12	
Costs of reworking	30	
Customer services relating to G3 faults	43	
Administration	25	
Selling and distribution	35	977
Net operating profit		83

The directors of Gill Ltd are concerned about the high cost of quality relating to G3. Guaranteed fault-free supplies of G3 could be obtained from the supplier at a 15% higher purchase price per unit.

Required:

(a) Explain what is meant by 'explicit' costs of quality.

(b) Identify the explicit costs of quality incurred by Gill Ltd in the year ended 31 December 2004.

(c) Explain what is meant by 'implicit' costs of quality and give one example of such costs for Gill Ltd for the year ended 31 December 2004.

(d) Advise the directors of Gill Ltd as to whether the fault-free supplies of G3 at the higher price would be worthwhile.

5.9 The managers of Lodden plc have decided to launch a new product, XL, at a selling price of £375 per unit. Market research suggests that sales of 18,000 units of XL should be achieved in the next year at this selling price. Lodden plc has a target level of operating profit of 20% on sales for this product.

Required:

(a) Calculate:

(i) the expected total sales revenue from XL for the next year

(ii) the target operating profit required by Lodden plc from sales of XL for the next year

(iii) the total target cost for XL for the next year

(iv) the target cost per unit of XL

(b) Explain briefly how value engineering may be used by Lodden plc in order to achieve the target cost per unit of XL.

5.10 Nett plc is a manufacturer of computers and related products. The managers of Nett plc are considering developing a processor for a number of specialised applications. The processor would have a relatively short life cycle, for which the following forecasts have been made:

- research, development and design would cost £60,000
- sales would take place over the following 3 years
- production costs would be £120,000 per year for 3 years plus £50 per unit
- selling and distribution costs would be £80,000 per year for 3 years plus £40 per unit
- customer support would cost £95,000 per year for 3 years and £75,000 per year for a further 2 years
- the total sales demand for the processor over the whole of its life cycle has been estimated at two possible prices:

  Case 1: 5,000 units at £400 per unit

  Case 2: 4,500 units at £480 per unit

Required:

(a) Calculate for each of the two possible selling prices per unit:

(i) the total life cycle sales revenue from the processor

(ii) the total life cycle costs of the processor (assuming production and sales volumes are equal)

(iii) the total life cycle profit from the processor

(b) Make a recommendation to the managers of Nett plc regarding the processor, given that the company's target level of profit is 30% on sales.

6 MEASURING PERFORMANCE

6.1 (a) What are performance indicators used for?

(b) Why are comparisons more useful than individual figures?

(c) List three kinds of comparisons which are useful.

6.2 The following profit and loss accounts relate to a wholesale trader selling electrical accessories such as cables, switches and so on:

M. Lomas: Profit and Loss Account for the year ended:

	30 June 2004		*30 June 2003*	
	£000s	*£000s*	*£000s*	*£000s*
Sales		780		675
Less: Cost of Sales				
Opening stock	60		90	
Purchases	520		410	
Less: Closing Stock	(40)	540	(60)	440
Gross Profit		240		235
Less: Expenses:				
Administration	60		45	
Selling	40	100	30	75
Net Profit		140		160

Required:

Calculate the following ratios for M. Lomas for the given years (correct to 1 decimal place):

- gross profit percentage
- net profit percentage
- each expense as a percentage of sales

Comment briefly on the original figures and on the percentages calculated.

6.3 The following are extracts from the financial accounts of Robins Ltd, manufacturers of artificial Christmas trees.

Robins Ltd: Extract from Profit and Loss Account
for the year ended 30 September:

	2004	*2003*
	£000s	*£000s*
Turnover	2,000	1,920
Operating Profit	267	240

Balance Sheet extract as at 30 September:

	2004		2003	
	£000s	*£000s*	*£000s*	*£000s*
Fixed assets (Net Book Value)		900		840
Current Assets:	120		110	
Current liabilities	(130)	(10)	(90)	20
Net Assets		890		860
Long-term loans		(50)		–
		840		860

Required:

(a) State the formulae for the following ratios and calculate them for Robins Ltd for the given years, (correct to 2 decimal places):

- return on capital employed
- asset turnover
- operating profit margin

(b) What is the relationship between the three ratios in (a)?

(c) Referring to the relationship between the ratios, identify the reason for the change in the ROCE from the first to second year.

6.4 Craig Ltd is a wholesaler, trading in plastics and specialised paints. Operating statements are given below for Craig Ltd for the years ended 31 December 2003 and 2004, together with balance sheet extracts as at those dates.

Craig Ltd: Operating Statements for the years ended 31 December

	2004		2003	
	£000s	£000s	£000s	£000s
Sales		602		587
Less: Cost of Sales				
Opening stock	14		38	
Purchases	428		375	
Less: closing stock	(20)	422	(14)	399
Gross Profit		180		188
Administration	64		62	
Selling and distribution	46	110	36	98
Operating profit		70		90

Craig Ltd: Balance Sheet Extracts as at 31 December

	2004		2003	
	£000s	£000s	£000s	£000s
Fixed assets at cost		330		300
Accumulated depreciation		(80)		(50)
		250		250
Current assets:				
Stock	20		14	
Debtors	73		58	
Cash at bank	-		12	
	93		84	
Current liabilities:				
Creditors	38		35	
Bank overdraft	2		-	
	40		35	
Net current assets		53		49
Net assets		303		299

Required:

(a) Identify the **two** most significant changes (from 2003 to 2004) in the given data for Craig Ltd

(b) For Craig Ltd for the given years, calculate:

(i) gross profit margin on sales

(ii) operating profit margin on sales

(iii) return on capital employed

(iv) asset turnover

(v) average age of debtors in days

(vi) average age of stock in days (using average stock)

(vii) average creditors' payment period in days

(viii) current ratio

(ix) quick (acid test) ratio

(c) Identify the **two** most significant changes (from 2003 to 2004) in the ratios you have calculated in (b) and comment briefly on possible reasons for these changes.

6.5 Laito Dairies Ltd is a chain of dairies (which process, bottle and distribute milk products) of which Newtown Dairy is one local division. The information below relates to Newtown Dairy.

Newtown Dairy: report for the year ended 31 July 2004

Summary Profit and Loss Account for the year ended 31 July 2004

	£000s	£000s
Turnover		1,300
Less: Cost of Sales		
Opening Stock	2	
Cost of Production	540	
Less: Closing Stock	(4)	538
Gross Profit		762
Administration	250	
Selling and Distribution	360	610
Operating Profit		152

Balance Sheet extract as at 31 July 2004:

	£000s	£000s	£000s
Fixed assets	*Land and Buildings*	*Plant*	*Total*
At cost	800	1,200	2,000
Additions	–	300	300
	800	1,500	2,300
Accumulated depreciation	–	600	600
	800	900	1,700
Current Assets:			
Raw materials stock	3		
Finished goods stock	4		
Debtors	45		
Cash at bank	25		
	77		
Current liabilities	(110)		(33)
Net Assets			1,667

Required (working correct to 1 decimal place):

(a) Calculate the following ratios for Newtown Dairy for the given year:

- gross profit margin
- operating profit margin
- return on capital employed (ROCE)
- asset turnover
- the average age of debtors
- the average age of finished goods stock (using average stock)

(b) Stating the formulae you are using, calculate the current and quick (acid test) ratios for Newtown Dairy and identify one feature of the business which has an effect on these ratios in this case.

(c) The directors of Laito Dairies Ltd consider that ROCE and Asset Turnover are important performance measures, and Newtown Dairy has failed to meet the company targets, which are:

Target ROCE: 15%   Target Asset turnover: 1.2 times

Assuming that the given balance sheet data is unchanged, calculate:

(i) the amount of Operating Profit which Newtown Dairy would have obtained in the given year if it had achieved the company target level of ROCE

(ii) the amount of Turnover which Newtown Dairy would have obtained if it had achieved the company target level of Asset Turnover

6.6 A summary of the trading account for Wold Ltd for a given year is as follows:

	£
Sales	285,000
Less: returns	1,200
	283,800
Cost of sales	198,660
Gross profit	85,140

Required:

(a) Calculate the closing debtors figure for Wold Ltd for the given year if all the sales are on credit and the average age of closing debtors is 1.2 months.

(b) Calculate the closing stock figure for Wold Ltd for the given year if the average age of closing stock is 2 months.

(c) Calculate the closing creditors figure for Wold Ltd for the given year if the cost of sales includes £201,760 of credit purchases and the average age of closing creditors is 1.5 months.

6.7 Walkers Ltd operates a chain of retail shoe shops. Walkers Ltd uses common accounting policies in all branches. The method of straight-line depreciation is used for fixed assets, which are mainly fixtures and fittings. The shops are rented, rent being included in 'other costs' below.

Branch managers are responsible for the control of stock and debtors and payments to creditors, but cash received is all paid into the Walkers Ltd bank account the same day.

Financial data relating to the Redridge Branch of Walkers Ltd is shown on the next page.

Walkers Ltd Redridge Branch Year ended 31 March 2004

Operating Statement for the year ended 31 March 2004

	£000s	*£000s*
Turnover		540.0
Less: Cost of Sales		
Opening Stock	70.0	
Purchases	270.0	
Less Closing Stock	(59.2)	280.8
Gross Profit		259.2
Wages and salaries	135.0	
Depreciation	22.0	
Other costs	45.5	202.5
Operating profit		56.7

Operating net assets as at 31 March 2004

	£000s	*£000s*
Fixed Assets at cost		220.0
Accumulated depreciation		88.0
Net Book Value		132.0
Working capital:		
Stock	59.2	
Debtors	27.0	
Creditors	(45.0)	41.2
Net assets		173.2

Required:

(a) For Walkers Ltd Redridge Branch, for the given year, calculate:

- return on capital employed
- gross profit margin as a percentage
- asset turnover
- operating profit margin as a percentage
- the average age of debtors in days

- the average age of creditors in days
- the average age of stock (using closing stock) in days

(b) The directors of Walkers Ltd have set certain targets which they consider the branches should be able to achieve. These targets are:

ROCE	37.5%
Asset Turnover	3.5 times per year
Average age of debtors	15 days
Average age of creditors	65 days
Average age of closing stock	70 days

(i) If Redridge Branch had achieved the company target level of Asset Turnover, while maintaining prices and the existing capital employed, what percentage would the ROCE have been?

(ii) If Redridge Branch had achieved the company targets for the average age of debtors, average age of creditors and average age of closing stock, while maintaining the same turnover and profit, what would the ROCE and the Asset Turnover have been?

(c) Comment briefly on the results for the Redridge Branch for the given year and its performance in relation to the Walkers Ltd targets. State two limitations of the use of ratios in this way for Walkers Ltd to measure the performance of its branch managers.

6.8 Lime plc is a manufacturer of roofing materials for industrial buildings and its results for the year ended 31 March 2004 are shown below.

Lime plc Summary Profit and Loss Account for the year ended 31 March 2004

	£000s	*£000s*
Turnover		932
Less: sales returns		(10)
		922
Less: Cost of Sales		
Opening stock	38	
Cost of Production	484	
Less: closing stock	(43)	479
Gross Profit		443
Administration	138	
Selling and distribution	165	303
Operating profit		140

Lime plc Summary Balance Sheet Extract as at 31 March 2004

	£000s	£000s
Fixed assets at cost		815
Accumulated depreciation		272
		543
Current assets:		
Raw materials stock	12	
Finished goods stock	43	
Debtors	150	
Cash	6	
	211	
Current liabilities	(84)	127
		670
Long-term liabilities: debentures		(50)
		620

Required:

(a) Calculate for Lime plc for the year ended 31 March 2004:

- (i) Gross profit margin
- (ii) Operating profit margin
- (iii) Return on capital employed (ROCE)
- (iv) Asset turnover
- (v) Average age of finished goods stock (using closing stock) in months
- (vi) Debtors' collection period in months

(b) Comment briefly on the results for Lime plc for the year ended 31 March 2004, given the additional information:

- the normal credit terms allowed to customers by Lime plc state that payment is due within 30 days
- in February 2003, the management of Lime plc had set the following targets for the year ended 31 March 2004:

  Return on capital employed 22.5%

  Operating profit margin 15%
- several machines used in production were replaced by new ones in December 2003. The new machines are more efficient. There is lower demand for Lime plc's products in the Winter, so the replacement work did not affect production.

7 MEASURING PERFORMANCE – FURTHER ASPECTS

7.1 Turnover and net profit figures are given in the following spreadsheet for Ray Ltd for the five years ended 31 December 2009.

Required: Enter suitable spreadsheet formulas in rows 5, 6 and 7, cells B to F. Show separately the results that would be obtained in those cells.

Comment on the results obtained.

	A	B	C	D	E	F
1	Year	2005	2006	2007	2008	2009
2	Turnover (£000s)	358	362	365	366	373
3	Net Profit (£000s)	55	57	59	60	62
4	Industry index	131	134	136	137	140
5	Turnover in 2009 terms (£000s)					
6	Net profit in 2009 terms (£000s)					
7	Net profit percentage in 2009 terms					

7.2 The following information is given for Ray Ltd for the year ended 31 December 2009.

Turnover	£373,000
Number of employees	20
Cost of materials used	£80,000
Total cost of bought-in services	£120,000

Required: calculate the total value added and the value added per employee for the year ended 31 December 2009 for Ray Ltd.

7.3 The following information is given for VAC Ltd for the year ended 31 August 2004.

Turnover	£590,000
Output (product units)	40,000
Number of employees	35
Cost of materials used	£130,000
Total cost of bought-in services	£195,000
Total cost of inputs	£325,000

Required: calculate for VAC Ltd for the year ended 31 August 2004:

- total value added
- value added per employee
- material cost per unit
- total cost of inputs per unit

7.4 For each of the following activities or aspects of work, suggest a suitable *non-financial indicator* which could be used to measure performance.

Activity or aspect to be measured

- Quality of installation service for kitchen units
- Output of carpets
- Customer satisfaction with a hotel
- Theatre ticket telephone booking service
- Website mail order books
- In-house accountancy training

7.5 Mann Ltd and Sett Ltd are two companies owned by Bow plc. Mann Ltd and Sett Ltd are similar companies using the same accounting policies. Both companies manufacture the same product, which is sold at the same price, to the house-building industry.

Financial and other information is given below for Mann Ltd, followed by certain performance indicators which have been calculated for Sett Ltd, for the year ended 31 March 2004.

Mann Ltd Income Statement: year to 31 March 2004

Units produced	15,000
Number of employees	12
	£000s
Turnover	1,750
Material and bought-in services	810
Production labour	210
Other production expenses	350
Depreciation – buildings	26
Depreciation – plant and machinery	90
Administration and other expenses	68
Operating profit	196

Mann Ltd: Extract from Balance Sheet as at 31 March 2004

	£000s	£000s	£000s
Fixed assets	*Cost*	*Provision for Depreciation*	*NBV*
Buildings	1,300	520	780
Plant and Machinery	900	540	360
	2,200	1,060	1,140
Net current assets			
Stock	34		
Debtors	27		
Cash	6		
Creditors	(42)		25
			1,165

Sett Ltd: Performance indicators for the year to 31 March 2004

• Units produced per employee (10 employees)	1,500
• Production labour cost per unit	£12
• Added value per employee	£95,000
• Asset turnover	0.8 times
• Operating profit margin	9.8%
• Return on capital employed	7.8%
• Operating profit per employee	£17,150
• Units per £1,000 of NBV of Fixed Assets	7

Required:

(a) Calculate for Mann Ltd the eight performance indicators (as listed above for Sett Ltd) for the year ended 31 March 2004.

(b) Explain what is meant by 'productivity' and 'efficiency' when referring to a profit-making organisation.

(c) From the eight performance indicators used by Bow plc above, suggest two which best measure efficiency and state whether Mann Ltd or Sett Ltd is more efficient.

(d) From the eight performance indicators used by Bow plc above, suggest two which best measure productivity and state whether Mann Ltd or Sett Ltd has higher productivity.

(e) Explain briefly one reason why the indicators may show one company to be more efficient, but the other to have higher productivity.

7.6 CRS Ltd produces a single product, for which the standard direct labour time is 1.5 hours per unit. For a given period, CRS Ltd budgeted for a total of 33,600 hours. The actual results for the period showed that 22,000 units were produced and the actual total direct labour hours worked were 32,500 hours.

Required: State the formulae and calculate the Efficiency Ratio, the Capacity Ratio and the Activity Ratio for CRS Ltd for this period.

7.7 You are employed by Park Ltd, a company with several subsidiaries and you have been asked to apply the balanced scorecard to monitor the performance of the subsidiaries. The following information relates to Subsidiary Green for the year ended 31 October 2004.

Subsidiary Green Profit and Loss Account for the year to 31 October 2004

	£000s	*£000s*
Sales		5,200
Less: returns		200
Turnover		5,000
Less: Cost of Sales		
Opening Finished Stock	140	
Cost of Production	1,800	
Closing Finished Stock	(170)	1,770
Gross Profit		3,230
Administration	340	
Product Development	410	
Selling and Distribution	290	
Customer Services	360	
Training	200	1,600
Operating Profit		1,630

Results of inspection of finished goods show that 2% are found to be faulty and are scrapped.

Analysis of turnover by products:	
Sales of new products	2,100
Sales of existing products	2,900
Turnover as above	5,000

Analysis of turnover by customers:	
Sales to new customers	1,250
Sales to existing customers	3,750
Turnover as above	5,000

Required:

(a) Identify and calculate, from the available information, one performance indicator which you could use in monitoring the financial perspective.

(b) Explain briefly what is meant by:

- The *customer perspective*
- The *internal perspective*
- The *innovation and learning perspective*

For each of these three perspectives, identify and calculate two possible performance indicators from the information given for Subsidiary Green.

7.8 You are employed by Micro Circuits Ltd as a financial analyst. One of your responsibilities is to monitor the performance of subsidiaries within the group. Financial and other data relating to subsidiary A is reproduced below.

Subsidiary A

Profit and Loss Account for the year to 30 November 2008

	£000s	*£000s*
Sales		4,000
Less returns		100
Turnover (note 1)		3,900
Material	230	
Labour	400	
Production overheads (note 2)	300	
Cost of production	930	
Opening finished stock	50	
Closing finished stock	(140)	
Cost of Sales		840
Gross Profit		3,060
Marketing	500	
Customer support	400	
Research and Development	750	
Training	140	
Administration	295	2,085
Operating Profit		975

Extract from Balance Sheet at 30 November 2008

	£000s	*£000s*	*£000s*
Fixed Assets	*Land and Buildings*	*Plant and Machinery*	*Total*
Cost	2,000	2,500	4,500
Additions	–	1,800	1,800

	2,000	4,300	6,300
Accumulated depreciation	160	1,700	1,860
	1,840	2,600	4,440
Raw material stock	15		
Finished goods stock	140		
	155		
Debtors	325		
Cash and Bank	40		
Creditors	(85)		
			435
Net assets			4,875

Notes

1 Analysis of Turnover

	£000s		*£000s*
Regular customers	3,120	New products	1,560
New customers	780	Existing products	2,340
	3,900		3,900

2 Production overheads include £37,200 of reworked faulty production

3 Orders received in the year totalled £4,550,000

Required:

Calculate the following performance indicators for Subsidiary A for the year to 30 November 2008:

(a) the return on capital employed

(b) the asset turnover

(c) the sales (or operating profit) margin

(d) the average age of debtors in months

(e) the average age of finished stock in months

(f) **two** performance indicators, for which the data is already recorded, which could be used to measure quality in Micro Circuits Ltd subsidiaries. Show how your suggested indicators would be calculated

(g) the average delay in fulfilling orders

7.9 Allen Ltd is a wholesaler of electrical goods. The operating statement for Allen Ltd for the year ended 31 December 2004 is shown below, together with a simplified Balance Sheet as at that date.

The managers of Allen Ltd are concerned about the company's bank account being overdrawn and are considering improving the control of debtors and reducing the company's costs. They require the Operating Statement and the Balance Sheet to be re-drafted to show what the results would have been if all the following conditions had been applied:

- the debtors' payment period had been reduced to 1 month
- the administration costs had been reduced by £24,000
- the selling and distribution costs had been reduced by £6,000

Allen Ltd Operating Statement for the year ended 31 December 2004

	£000s	*£000s*
Turnover		468
Less: Cost of Sales		
Opening Stock	55	
Purchases	250	
Less: closing stock	(24)	281
Gross Profit		187
Administration Costs	92	
Selling and Distribution expenses	46	138
Operating profit		49

Allen Ltd Balance Sheet as at 31 December 2004

	£000s	*£000s*
Fixed Assets at cost		360
Less: accumulated depreciation		150
		210
Current Assets:		
Stock	24	
Debtors	69	
Cash at Bank	-	
	93	
Current Liabilities:		
Creditors	52	
Bank overdraft	11	
	63	
Net current assets		30
		240

Financed by:	
Ordinary shares issued and fully paid	160
Retained Profits	80
	240

Required:

For Allen Ltd for the year ended 31 December 2004:

(a) Calculate the following ratios from the given data:

- Gross Profit as a percentage of Turnover
- Operating Profit as a percentage of Turnover
- Return on Capital Employed
- Asset Turnover

(b) Re-draft the Operating Statement and the Balance Sheet according to the three requirements of the managers of Allen Ltd.

(c) Calculate the same four ratios as in (a) for the revised data prepared in (b).

(d) Comment briefly on the results of your calculations.

7.10 Ravensdale is a nursing home run by a charitable trust. There are currently 30 residents. The following data relates to Ravensdale for the year ended 31 March 2004.

Ravensdale Operating Statement for the year ended 31 March 2004

	£	£
Income from Fees		546,000
Less: expenses		
Care of residents		
(variable with number of residents)	270,000	
Management and administration	55,000	
General expenses	81,000	
Depreciation of equipment and vehicles	88,000	494,000
Operating surplus		52,000

Ravensdale Summary of Net Assets as at 31 March 2004

	Premises	*Equipment & vehicles*	*Total*
Fixed Assets	£	£	£
Cost	980,000	440,000	1,420,000
Depreciation to date		176,000	176,000
	980,000	264,000	1,244,000
Current assets			
Debtors	68,250		
Cash at bank	30,450		
	98,700		
Creditors (for General Expenses)	13,500		
Net current assets			85,200
Net assets			1,329,200

Required:

(a) Calculate:

(i) debtors' collection period in months

(ii) payment period for creditors (which all relate to general expenses) in months

(iii) total cash-based expenses (expenses other than depreciation)

(iv) the number of months of cash based expenses that could be paid from the cash at bank

(b) The following changes will take place in the next year (the year ended 31 March 2005):

- there will be 3 more residents and, as a result, fee income and the cost of care of residents will both increase by 10%
- new equipment will be purchased at a cost of £60,000 and the total depreciation charge (on equipment and vehicles) for the year will be £100,000
- the debtors' collection period will be reduced to 1 month
- the creditors' payment period will be reduced to 1.5 months

Taking account of all these changes, prepare a forecast operating statement and summary of net assets for Ravensdale for the year ended 31 March 2005.

Hint:

Net assets at 31 March 2005 =

Net assets at 31 March 2004 + surplus for the year ended 31 March 2005

After using this equation, cash at bank can be found as a balancing figure.

8 USING BUDGETS

8.1 List and explain briefly **three** of the main advantages of budgeting for an organisation.

8.2 Explain what is meant by the term 'key (or principal) budget factor'. What is the most common key budget factor for a manufacturing company? Suggest a possible key budget factor for a charity.

8.3 The deseasonalised data for sales volumes of product Alpha for the four quarters of Year 3 is as follows:

Quarter 1: 20,400 units

Quarter 2: 20,715 units

Quarter 3: 21,020 units

Quarter 4: 21,300 units

The average percentage seasonal variations in sales volume for Alpha have been calculated as:

Quarter	1	2	3	4
	–20%	–10%	–	+30%

Required:

Calculate the forecast sales volume of Alpha for each of the four quarters of Year 4, assuming that the year 3 trend and the average seasonal variations will continue.

8.4 The actual sales revenue for product Beta for the four quarters of Year 3 was as follows:

Quarter 1: £53,600

Quarter 2: £56,650

Quarter 3: £62,610

Quarter 4: £64,600

The average absolute (additive) seasonal variations in sales revenue for Beta have been calculated as:

Quarter	1	2	3	4
	– £5,000	– £2,500	+ £3,000	+ £4,500

Required:

(a) Calculate the deseasonalised trend in sales revenue for product Beta for Year 3.

(b) Calculate the forecast sales revenue for Beta for each of the four quarters of Year 4, assuming that the Year 3 trend and the average seasonal variations will continue.

(c) Explain briefly any reservations you may have about the validity of the forecasts in answer (b).

8.5 In Year 3, the direct materials used by a manufacturer of plumbing accessories included:

Material W: at £3.20 per kg

Material X: at £8.50 per kg

and the average wages paid included:

Skilled production wages: £6.80 per hour

Supervisors: £22,000 per annum.

The following index numbers are available:

	Year 3	*Year 4 forecast*
Plumbing accessory prices	103	102
Materials prices (type W)	128	130
Materials prices (type X)	115	119
National average wages	187	190

Required:

(a) Calculate forecast costs for Year 4, for the materials and wages listed above.

(b) Explain briefly any reservations you may have about the forecasts calculated in (a).

8.6 Boxco Ltd is a manufacturer of heavy-duty cardboard packing cases. Two sheets of cardboard are required to make each packing case. The following forecasts are available for January 2004:

Forecast sales demand = 1,750 packing cases

Stocks as at:	1 January 2004	31 January 2004
Finished packing cases	550	500
Cardboard sheets	880	920

Required:

(a) For Boxco Ltd for January 2004, calculate the following:

- production budget in units (packing cases)
- materials usage budget in units (cardboard sheets)
- materials purchases budget in units (cardboard sheets)

(b) By considering the methods you have used in part (a), enter suitable formulae in the blank cells in columns B and C of the following spreadsheet format.

	A	B	C
1	*Month*	*January*	*February*
2	Sales forecast (packing cases)	1,750	2,000
3	Opening Finished Goods Stock	550	
4	Closing Finished Goods Stock	500	540
5	Production units (packing cases)		
6	Material usage per product unit	2	
7	Material usage for month (sheets)		
8	Opening Material Stock (sheets)	880	
9	Closing Material Stock (sheets)	920	950
10	Material Purchases units (sheets)		

8.7 Sunny Ltd is a manufacturer of moulded plastic toys. The standard cost of a garden toy is as follows:

0.9 kg of plastic at £0.80 per kg

0.25 hours of direct labour at £6.60 per hour

Fixed production overheads absorbed at £3.50 per unit

(Absorption rate based on budgeted production of 7,500 toys per quarter)

The selling price of this toy is £9.00.

The forecast sales volumes for this toy for the first three months of the year 2004 are:

	January	*February*	*March*
Sales units (toys)	1,800	2,000	2,300

The stock levels as at 1 January 2004 are planned to be:

Finished goods stock: 200 toys

Raw materials stock: 750 kg of plastic

It is planned to increase finished goods stocks by 200 toys per month and increase raw materials stocks by 100 kg per month, in anticipation of higher sales in Summer.

Required:

(a) Calculate the following for each of the first three months of 2004 and in total for the quarter:

- The production volume budget (number of toys)
- The raw materials usage budget in kg of plastic and in £
- The raw materials purchases budget in kg of plastic and in £
- The direct labour utilisation budget in hours and in £

(b) Using your answers to (a) set out a quarterly budgeted manufacturing and trading account for the quarter ended 31 March 2004 for this toy (ie using totals calculated in (a) for the quarter). Use absorption costing and show the adjustment to gross profit for any over or under absorption of fixed production overheads which would occur in this quarter.

8.8 Alder Ltd manufactures two products, AL1 and AL2, both of which are made from two materials, X and Y. The following data relates to Alder Ltd's next budget period.

Raw materials:	**X**	**Y**
Opening stock	8,000 kg	6,000 kg
Closing stock	11,000 kg	4,500 kg
Price per kg	£2.60	£4.10

Product:	**AL1**	**AL2**
Forecast sales (units)	12,500	15,000
Opening stock (units)	2,000	2,000
Closing stock (units)	4,000	1,000
Material X per product unit	2.0 kg	3.0 kg
Material Y per product unit	1.5 kg	2.0 kg
Direct labour hours per product unit	0.5 hours	1.5 hours

The total cost of Direct Labour is a step cost:

£165,000 for up to 27,500 hours

£175,000 for more than 27,500 and up to 29,000 hours

£185,000 for more than 29,000 and up to 30,500 hours

Required:

Calculate for Alder Ltd for the given budget period

(a) the production volume required for each of the products AL1 and AL2

(b) the quantities of each of the materials X and Y required for production

(c) the quantities of each of the materials X and Y to be purchased

(d) the total hours of direct labour required

(e) the material purchases budget in £ for each of the materials X and Y

(f) the total cost of direct labour for the period

8.9 Briar Ltd manufactures two products, BR1 and BR2, both of which are made from two materials, W and Z. Forecast total sales for the next year are 78,400 units of BR1 and 60,000 units of BR2. Analysis has shown that sales of BR1 are evenly spread through the year, but sales of BR2 are subject to additive (absolute) quarterly seasonal variations. The variations in sales of BR2 around the average are expected to be:

Quarter	1	2	3	4
Seasonal variation (units of BR2)	-800	+400	+700	-300

The following data for Briar Ltd relates to the budget for Quarter 1 of the next year.

Raw materials:	**W**	**Z**
Opening stock	10,000 kg	5,600 kg
Closing stock	9,000 kg	6,200 kg
Price per kg	£8.00	£1.80

Product:	**BR1**	**BR2**
Opening stock (units)	8,200	2,800
Closing stock (units)	4,000	3,000
Material W per product unit	4.0 kg	2.5 kg
Material Z per product unit	0.7 kg	1.2 kg
Direct labour hours per product unit	2.0 hours	1.5 hours

Direct Labour is a variable cost: £5.85 per hour. In addition to the hours required for production, 1,500 hours are to be allowed for training, to be paid at the same rate.

Required:

Calculate for Briar Ltd for Quarter 1 of the next year

(a) the expected sales volume for each of the products BR1 and BR2

(b) the production volume required for each of the products BR1 and BR2

(c) the quantities of each of the materials W and Z required for production

(d) the quantities of each of the materials W and Z to be purchased

(e) the total hours of direct labour required for production

(f) the material purchases budget in £ for each of the materials W and Z

(g) the total cost of direct labour for the period

8.10 Cork Ltd manufactures two products, C and K, using the same material, M. The price of material M is forecast to rise significantly and the managers of Cork Ltd have decided to budget for no more than £252,000 to be spent on Material M in a four-week period. For the next four-week budget period, Cork Ltd will have opening stocks of 1,000 kg of M and will require closing stocks of 500 kg. There will be no opening or closing stocks of the finished products C and K.

Cork Ltd is contracted to sell 4,000 units of C in the period and will use any remaining material M to make as many units of product K as possible.

The materials and labour required for the two products are as follows:

Product	**C**	**K**
Direct material M per product unit	3 kg	5 kg
Direct labour hours per product unit	0.50 hours	1.25 hours

Cork Ltd has 32 direct workers, who normally work 39 hours per week. Overtime is used for any further hours required.

The price of material M was £9.00 per kg when a suitable index was at 108. The index is expected to be 126 in the next four-week budget period.

Required:

For Cork Ltd for the next four-week budget period, calculate

(a) the expected price per kg of material M

(b) the quantity of material M that can be purchased

(c) the quantity of material M that can be used in production of product K

(d) the number of units of product K that can be made and sold

(e) the total direct labour hours required for products C and K during the period

(f) the number of hours of overtime required

9 PRACTICAL ASPECTS OF BUDGET PREPARATION

9.1 The forecast demand for a component for a given period is 7,600 units. It is known that on average 5% of the finished components are rejected on final inspection.

If finished component stock levels are to remain unchanged, calculate the required units to be produced.

9.2 The forecast demand for a product for a given period is 5,300 units. The opening finished goods stock is 800 units and the required closing stock is 300 units. It is known that 4% of the product units on average are faulty and have to be scrapped.

Calculate the total production budget in units.

9.3 The standard direct labour time for a product is 2 hours per unit. 9,750 units of the product are to be produced in a given period. A new training initiative is to be brought in during the period, which will result in 2.5% of the direct labour time being used for training.

Calculate the total direct labour hours to be budgeted for the period.

9.4 The standard direct labour time for a product is 1 hour per product unit. Required production in a given period is 2,200 units. Following a new agreement on working methods, it is expected that 110% efficiency will be achieved in this period.

Calculate the labour hours to be budgeted for the required production.

9.5 The sales demand for a product in the next six months is expected to be 13,000 units. The opening finished goods stock is expected to be 1,460 units, and it is required to have 1,000 units in stock at the end of the six month period. On average, 5% of the units produced are rejected on inspection. The standard direct labour hours are 1.5 hours per unit, but this is a relatively new product and only 90% efficiency is expected in the period.

Calculate the hours to be budgeted for direct labour for the six month period.

9.6 Party Ltd is a manufacturer of paper plates. In cutting and forming the plates, 22% of the paper material is wasted. After cutting and forming, 2% of the plates have faults and are scrapped. Each batch of 100 finished plates weighs 1 kg and consists entirely of the paper material.

For the next period of production, the opening and closing stock levels are to be as follows:

	Paper (raw material)	*Plates (finished goods)*
Opening stock	200 kg	20,360 plates
Closing stock	350 kg	19,000 plates

The demand for finished plates for the period is 460,000 plates.

Required:

Calculate:

- the good production required
- the total production required
- the amount of paper needed to commence production
- the amount of paper required to be purchased

9.7 Green Ltd is a manufacturer of garden furniture. The forecast monthly demand for its garden chairs for the year 2004 is as follows:

2004 Forecast sales volume (Number of chairs):

January	3,000	July	25,000
February	8,000	August	20,000
March	15,000	September	15,000
April	20,000	October	4,000
May	20,000	November	2,000
June	25,000	December	2,000

Green Ltd's stock policy is to have 30% of the next month's demand in stock at the end of each month. The stock of chairs at 1 January 2004 and at 31 December 2004 is expected to be 900 chairs. The direct labour hours available per month in Green Ltd (without any overtime working) are sufficient to make 22,000 chairs.

Required:

(a) Calculate the required monthly production of chairs in line with Green Ltd's stock policy.

(b) (i) Explain how production could be rescheduled in order to avoid the necessity for overtime. State the monthly production required to do this without stock levels falling below the levels stated in the current policy.

(ii) State the closing stock of chairs at the end of each month in your revised production schedule.

(c) What further information would you require in order to decide whether it would be better for Green Ltd to reschedule production or to use direct labour overtime to complete the production according to the original budget?

(d) Suggest two other alternative courses of action open to the management of Green Ltd, which would enable them to satisfy the demand for their garden chairs.

9.8 Kale Ltd manufactures two products, K and L, using two materials, U and V. The following data relates to Kale Ltd for the next budget period.

Product	**K**	**L**
Sales (units)	5,950	7,600
Opening stock (units)	200	750
Closing stock (units)	250	750
Material U per product unit of output	-	0.5 m
Material V per product unit of output	2.0 m	1.0 m
Direct labour per product unit	1.0 hours	0.8 hours

Material	**U**	**V**
Opening stock	900 m	800 m
Closing stock	500 m	1,400 m
Wastage during production	5%	2%

Required:

Calculate for Kale Ltd for the next budget period

(a) production volume required for each of the products K and L

(b) quantity of each of the materials U and V required for production output

(c) quantity of each of the materials U and V for input to production

(d) quantity of each of the materials U and V to be purchased

(e) the direct labour hours required for production

(f) the total direct labour hours to be paid for, if an additional 2% of production time is to be allowed for setting up machinery

9.9 Lewis Ltd manufactures two products, Jay and Kay, using the same material and the same direct labour force. The original budget data for the next quarter is as follows. There is no budgeted finished goods stock at the beginning or end of the quarter. Fixed overheads are absorbed on the basis of £30 per product unit.

Product	**Demand**	**Costs per unit**		
		Direct material	Direct labour	Fixed overhead
Jay	2,840 units	£56	£18	£30
Kay	3,360 units	£50	£14	£30

The material costs £4 per kg. Direct material and direct labour are variable costs. The selling prices of the products are £127 per unit of Jay and £120 per unit of Kay.

The direct material used by Lewis Ltd is in short supply and the company will be able to obtain only 70,000 kg for production in the next quarter. The direct labour hours needed for full production are available.

Required:

(a) Calculate the quantity of material that would be needed by Lewis Ltd for production of the full demand for Jay and Kay in the next quarter.

(b) Taking into account the limit on the supply of material, produce a revised production budget in units for the next quarter that maximises profit for Lewis Ltd.

(c) Calculate the total budgeted contribution that Lewis Ltd would obtain in the next quarter using your production budget from (b) and assuming all production is sold.

(d) Calculate the total budgeted fixed overhead and the budgeted profit for Lewis Ltd for the next quarter, using your answer to part (c).

9.10 Glynn Ltd manufactures three products, L, Y and N, using the same material and the same two grades of direct labour.

The original budget data for the next quarter is as follows. There is no budgeted finished goods stock at the beginning or end of the quarter.

Product	Demand	Variable Costs per unit		
		Direct material	Direct labour Grade I	Direct labour Grade II
L	7,800 units	£32	£32	£27
Y	3,800 units	£44	£48	£54
N	8,000 units	£23	£16	£6

Supplies of the material are unlimited. Direct material and both grades of direct labour are variable costs. The selling prices of the products are £210 per unit of L, £300 per unit of Y and £100 per unit of N.

The Grade II direct labour hours needed for full production are available, but Grade I workers are currently in short supply. Glynn Ltd has started a training programme to improve the situation. There are two cases to consider for the next quarter, depending on the number of trainees completing the training programme:

(i) 58,000 Grade I direct labours hours will be available

(ii) 70,250 Grade I direct labour hours will be available

The direct labour rate for Grade I is £6.40 per hour. The fixed costs amount to £1,250,000 per quarter.

Required:

(a) Calculate the contribution per unit for each of the products L, Y and N

(b) Calculate the contribution per unit per hour of Grade I direct labour for each of the products and hence rank the products for best use of this limited resource

(c) For each of the cases (i) and (ii), prepare revised production budgets in units to maximise profit for the next quarter

(d) Calculate the total contribution and hence the profit resulting from each of your answers in part (c)

(e) Comment briefly on the factors other than quarterly profit maximisation that the managers of Glynn Ltd should take into account when setting production budgets during the period of shortage of Grade I labour

10 APPLICATION OF BUDGETING METHODS

10.1 Incremental budgeting is used by Pastel Papers Ltd, a company which manufactures stationery products. Company administration salaries for last year amounted to £180,000. The company has expansion plans which are expected to result in £30,000 of additional administration salaries (estimated at current prices). Forecast inflation is expected to result in a 2% increase in such salaries.

What would be the Pastel Papers Ltd budget for administration salaries for the coming year, using incremental budgeting?

10.2 (a) List and explain briefly the advantages and disadvantages of incremental budgeting.

(b) In what circumstances are

(i) zero base budgeting

(ii) programme based budgeting

most likely to be appropriate?

10.3 Production overheads in a manufacturing company have been identified as semi-variable. They consist of fixed costs of £220,000 plus £5.10 per unit produced, for a range of levels of production from 25,000 units to 40,000 units for the period.

Required:

(a) Calculate the total production overheads for

(i) 30,000 units of production

(ii) 36,500 units of production

(b) Why would the same method not be appropriate for calculating the production overheads for 20,000 units or 50,000 units?

10.4 You are given the total of a semi-variable cost at four different levels of activity, as follows:

Level of activity (units)	500	780	1,000	1,200
Total cost (£)	1,875	2,141	2,350	2,540

Use the high-low method to calculate the variable cost per unit and the fixed part of this semi-variable cost.

10.5 Yare Ltd manufactures a single product, the Yare, and the budgeted costs of production are as follows (for levels of production between 10,000 and 16,000 units of Yare):

Direct material is a variable cost: £5.20 per unit of Yare produced

Direct labour is a semi-variable cost: £35,000 fixed cost plus £8.50 per unit of Yare produced

Production overhead is a semi-variable cost: £40,000 fixed cost plus £4.80 per unit of Yare produced.

Required:

For Yare Ltd

(a) Calculate the total costs of production for 12,000 units of Yare

(b) Enter formulas in cells B8 to B12 of the following spreadsheet, so that it could be used to calculate the budgeted production costs for any number of units of Yare within the relevant range and with any budgeted fixed and variable costs. The given data is shown as an example.

	A	B
1	Production volume (units of Yare)	12,000
2	Direct material: variable cost per unit of Yare (£)	5.20
3	Direct labour: variable cost per unit of Yare (£)	8.50
4	Direct labour: fixed cost (£)	35,000
5	Production overhead: variable cost per unit of Yare (£)	4.80
6	Production overhead: fixed cost (£)	40,000
7	**Budgeted production cost:**	**£**
8	Direct material	
9	Direct labour	
10	Production overhead	
11	Total budgeted production cost	
12	Budgeted production cost per unit	

10.6 The Bure Company makes a single product, PB. Budgets have been prepared for the company's production costs at two levels of activity: 20,000 units or 35,000 units of PB, as shown below. In this range of levels of activity, the direct costs are either variable or semi-variable and the production overheads are semi-variable.

The Bure Company Budgeted Production Costs

Production (units of PB)	20,000	35,000
	£	£
Direct material	30,000	52,500
Direct labour	198,000	294,000
Production overheads	130,000	186,250
Total production cost	358,000	532,750

Required:

For The Bure Company, calculate:

(a) the fixed and variable parts of each type of cost, using the high-low method

(b) the flexible production cost budget for 30,000 units of PB

10.7 SP-CARS plc is a manufacturer of sports cars, and one of its divisions (Seats Division) makes seats for the cars. The seats are all transferred at cost to another division of SP-CARS plc, to be fitted into the cars. The demand for seats therefore depends on the total production of cars in SP-CARS plc.

For the year to 30 September 2004, Seats Division prepared two provisional budgets, as shown below. They have been prepared on a basis which would apply to any level of demand from 5,000 to 7,500 seats. Over this range, the first three elements of cost shown are either variable or semi-variable. 'Rent, insurance and depreciation' behaves as a step cost. It is fixed for production from 5,000 to 6,250 seats, but increases by £5,000 per year when production exceeds 6,250 seats.

Seats Division provisional budgets: 12 months to 30 September 2004

Volume (number of Seats)	6,000	7,000
	£	£
Material	108,000	126,000
Labour	150,000	165,000
Power and Maintenance	31,600	33,200
Rent, Insurance and Depreciation	85,000	90,000
Total cost	374,600	414,200

After these budgets were prepared, it was estimated that 6,000 seats would be required, and the first budget above was set as the budget for the year.

During the year ended 30 September 2004, SP-CARS plc actually needed 6,300 seats and a performance statement was prepared, as shown below.

Seats Division performance statement: 12 months to 30 September 2004

	Budget	*Actual*	*Variance*
Volume (number of Seats)	6,000	6,300	
	£	£	£
Material	108,000	110,000	2,000 A
Labour	150,000	160,500	10,500 A
Power and Maintenance	31,600	28,000	3,600 F
Rent, Insurance and Depreciation	85,000	88,000	3,000 A
Total cost	374,600	386,500	11,900 A

Note: F=Favourable, A=Adverse

Required:

(a) Using the data given in the two provisional budgets, calculate the fixed and variable cost elements for Material, Labour and Power and Maintenance.

(b) On investigation of the significant adverse labour variance, it is found that an error had occurred in coding the actual costs. Maintenance costs of £2,500 had been coded to Labour. Adjust the actual results to correct this error.

Using your answers to (a), prepare an amended performance statement based on flexible budgeting. Show a flexed budget compared with the corrected actual results to give the (revised) variances.

(c) Explain briefly, with reference to the case of SP-CARS plc, why a flexible budget is preferable to a fixed budget for measuring performance.

10.8 Hillfield Ltd commenced the manufacture and sale of a single product, coded HFD, on 1 July 2004.

The original budget for Hillfield Ltd for the 3 months to 30 September 2004 planned for production and sales volumes to be equal, both being 1,500 HFDs.

The actual results for the period were that 1,400 HFDs were produced and only 1,100 sold. The budgeted and actual figures are given below, together with attached notes.

Hillfield Ltd: Operating results for 3 months ending 30 September 2004

	Budget	*Actual*
Sales volume (HFDs)	1,500	1,100
Production volume (HFDs)	1,500	1,400
	£	£
Sales	60,000	46,200
Less: Cost of Sales:		
Direct costs:		
Materials	7,500	6,380
Labour	9,000	7,150
Overheads:		
Production overheads	13,450	10,442
Total production cost of sales	29,950	23,972
Selling overheads	16,350	15,660
Total cost of sales	46,300	39,632
Profit	13,700	6,568

Notes:

(i) Direct materials and direct labour are both variable costs.

(ii) Production overheads are semi-variable. The budget for the fixed part is £10,000 for this level of activity. The actual fixed production overhead incurred was equal to the budget.

(iii) Selling overheads are semi-variable. The budget for the fixed part is £15,000. The remainder varies in relation to sales volume. The actual fixed selling overhead was equal to the budget.

(iv) There were no stocks of work-in-progress and no opening stocks of finished goods.

(v) To calculate the actual cost of sales in the statement above, the closing stocks were valued at actual production cost. The number of HFDs was used to apportion the actual production costs between the cost of sales and the closing stock. The composition of the production cost of sales and closing stock was therefore:

	Closing Stock	*Cost of Sales*	*Cost of Production*
Number of units (HFDs)	300	1,100	1,400
	£	£	£
Direct material	1,740	6,380	8,120
Direct labour	1,950	7,150	9,100
Production overhead	2,848	10,442	13,290
Production cost	6,538	23,972	30,510

Required:

(a) Calculate the following:

- the budgeted selling price per HFD
- the budgeted direct material cost per HFD
- the budgeted direct labour cost per HFD
- the budgeted marginal cost of production overhead per HFD
- the actual marginal cost of production overhead per HFD
- the budgeted marginal cost of selling overhead per HFD
- the actual marginal cost of selling overhead per HFD

(b) Prepare a flexible budget statement for the operating results of Hillfield Ltd for the 3 months to 30 September 2004, using marginal costing format and showing the variances.

(c) Explain briefly why the actual profit reported in the marginal costing statement for the 3 months to 30 September 2004 for Hillfield Ltd differs from the actual profit shown in the original statement. Show how the two profit figures can be reconciled.

10.9 State whether each of the following is TRUE or FALSE.

1 Zero base budgeting encourages changes in working methods.

2 Zero base budgeting encourages the introduction of budgetary slack into budgets.

3 A cost which is a constant amount per unit is described as fixed.

4 Marginal costing uses a cost for each unit of output based purely on variable costs.

5 A control period is the length of time for which a budget is prepared, usually a year.

6 It is not worthwhile to investigate favourable variances.

7 Comparing actual results with a flexible budget gives useful feedback for control purposes.

8 Feedforward might result in a revised version of the budget.

9 Variances which exceed the control limits should be identified and reported to the manager responsible.

10 Management reports should not include any non-financial information.

10.10 Bond plc is a manufacturer of robotic machines. The managers of Bond plc are considering developing a new machine. The machine would have a relatively short life cycle, for which the following forecasts have been made:

- research, development and design would cost £6.5million
- sales would take place over the following 3 years
- production costs would be £2.2million per year for 3 years plus £19,000 per unit
- customer support would cost £1million per year for 3 years
- the total sales demand for the machine over the whole of its life cycle has been estimated as 900 units at £55,000 each

Required:

(a) Calculate for the new machine being considered by Bond plc

(i) the total budgeted life cycle sales revenue from the machine

(ii) the total budgeted life cycle costs of the machine (assuming production and sales volumes are equal)

(iii) the total budgeted life cycle profit from the machine

(b) Explain briefly the advantages of life cycle budgeting for this type of product.

11 MANAGEMENT ISSUES IN RELATION TO BUDGETING

11.1 Management Accounting information is useful to managers for:

- reporting results
- highlighting problems that need action
- assisting with decision-making

Required:

(a) For each of the three purposes given above, give two examples of management accounting information which could be used.

(b) Explain briefly why management information is important to the senior managers of a large organisation.

(c) What is the starting point for the planning process for an organisation?

11.2 The following are short extracts from a Police Authority Budget and Performance Plan for the year 2004/2005.

1 the Authority's five-year Best Value programme is flexible and dynamic and is reviewed each year

2 investing in information technology and essential support services including dedicated police air support coverage

3 securing the maintenance of an efficient and effective police service throughout the county

4 making more police officers available for frontline duties

5 answer 90% of '999' calls within 10 seconds

6 minimum police strength of 1,475 officers by 31 March 2005

7 the Constabulary delivers service to clear standards covering both cost and quality

8 attend 88% of incidents requiring immediate response in rural areas within 20 minutes

9 responding to the community's request for more visible and accessible policing, thus reducing the fear of crime

10 no more violent crimes in this year in public places than in 2003/2004

Required: with reference to the extracts given above:

(a) Explain the term 'best value'.

(b) For each of the given extracts, state whether it relates to:

- long-term organisational goals or objectives
- strategies for achieving objectives
- short-term aims

(c) Explain briefly, using your answer to (b) as an illustration, how the long-term goals of an organisation can be expressed in short-term detailed budgets for sections of the organisation.

(d) Identify four measures of performance which could be used in the annual review, in which the level of achievement of the stated aims is assessed.

11.3 Required:

(a) Explain what is meant by the term 'controllable cost'.

(b) Explain why it is important for performance measurement to identify whether a cost is controllable by a particular manager.

11.4 The following information relates to Astro Screens Ltd, a manufacturer of computer screens. The company's organisational goals include continuous quality improvements as well as maximisation of profits.

There are four screen production departments, (SP1 – SP4), each making a particular type of screen. Department G produces a component which is transferred to the four SP departments, where it is used in the manufacture of the screens. The components are transferred at standard production cost and are not sold to other customers. The manager of Department G is responsible for the direct cost variances relating to production of the component.

Astro Screens Ltd has contracts to supply screens to ten computer manufacturers. Due to frequent changes in product specifications, the contracts are short-term and prices are re-negotiated by the managers of the SP (screen production) departments on a regular basis. The managers of the SP departments have responsibility for ensuring that the quality and delivery dates of supplies to customers can be guaranteed. They have the authority to appoint the skilled staff needed and arrange staff overtime. They are also authorised to invest in machinery or equipment necessary to do this, up to an agreed maximum for each department.

Required:

(a) For department G of Astro Screens Ltd, state whether it can be considered as

- a cost centre
- a profit centre
- an investment centre

(b) For department G of Astro Screens Ltd, suggest one reason why the transfer of components at standard production cost may not result in goal congruence.

(c) For the SP (screen production) departments of Astro Screens Ltd, state whether each department can be considered as

- a cost centre
- a profit centre
- an investment centre

(d) For the SP departments of Astro Screens Ltd, state whether the following items can be considered as controllable by each departmental manager

- sales revenue
- cost of components transferred from department G
- direct labour cost

(e) For the SP departmental managers in Astro Screens Ltd, suggest one financial and one non-financial measure of performance.

11.5 For the year ended 31 March 2004, the senior manager of North County Library Services introduced participative budgeting for the managers of main and branch libraries. Premises costs such as rent and rates and buildings maintenance are paid from a central budget for all the libraries in the county.

The following information relates to Eastwick (North County) Branch Library for the year ended 31 March 2004.

	Budget	*Actual*	*Variance*
	£	£	£
Library budget allocation	100,000	100,000	–
Other income (fines, charges photocopying, sales of maps, prints, old books etc.)	6,000	5,400	600 A
	106,000	105,400	600 A
Less:			
Staff salaries	85,000	85,600	600 A
Replacement books etc	7,800	7,650	150 F
Magazine subscriptions	3,200	3,350	150 A
Cleaning	2,600	2,700	100 A
Maintenance of fixtures	900	400	500 F
Depreciation of fixtures	1,800	1,800	–
Lease of photocopier	1,900	1,900	–
Heating and Lighting	2,800	2,000	800F
	106,000	105,400	600 F
Net surplus/deficit	nil	nil	nil

Required:

(a) Explain briefly what 'participative budgeting' implies for library managers.

(b) Suggest two reasons why the favourable variances shown above may have occurred, other than as a result of better motivation due to participative budgeting.

(c) Under what circumstances is it likely to be preferable for a senior manager to impose a budget, rather than take the participative approach?

11.6 Topp plc uses divisional profits as the basis for performance related pay for its divisional managers. The company's objectives include becoming a market leader for a complete range of high quality products as well as satisfying its share-holders with good returns on their investment.

Required:

(a) List three essential features for the success of Topp plc's performance related pay scheme.

(b) Suggest how a performance related pay scheme based on profits might encourage Topp plc's divisional managers to take action which does not lead to goal congruence.

11.7 You have recently been appointed as accountant to Claude Ltd, a small company manufacturing a specialised fertiliser. Part of the process involves using ovens which must be kept at a constant temperature all the time, even when empty. The power to heat the ovens does not therefore vary with changes in the amount of fertiliser being produced and so the cost of power is treated as a fixed cost.

The managing director, Emile Claude, shows you the following cost reports for the year ended 30 November 2004 and for the last quarter of that year, commenting that:

- the reports are not helpful for the purpose of managing the business
- he cannot understand why the direct material variance for the fourth quarter is favourable, when he is aware that the cost per unit of the material has been increasing throughout the year
- the direct labour variances, being adverse for the year and favourable for the quarter, seem incorrect, because the production workers have been paid the budgeted rate of £8 per hour throughout the year and no overtime was worked
- he is concerned that the power costs are so high in the fourth quarter even though output was below the budget

Claude Ltd Cost Report for the year ended 30 November 2004

	Budget		Actual		Variance
Units produced (tonnes)		12,000		13,000	1,000 F
	£	£	£	£	£
Direct material		144,000		188,500	44,500 A
Direct labour		192,000		227,500	35,500 A
Fixed overheads:					
Lease of machinery	60,000		60,000		–
Rent and rates	96,000		104,000		8,000 A
Insurance	48,000		52,000		4,000 A
Power	120,000		140,000		20,000 A
		324,000		356,000	
Total costs		660,000		772,000	112,000 A

Claude Ltd Cost Report for Quarter 4 of the year ended 30 November 2004

	Budget		Actual		Variance
Units produced (tonnes)		3,000		2,400	600 A
	£	£	£	£	£
Direct material		36,000		35,280	720 F
Direct labour		48,000		42,240	5,760 F
Fixed overheads:					
Lease of machinery	15,000		15,000		–
Rent and rates	24,000		26,000		2,000 A
Insurance	12,000		13,000		1,000 A
Power	30,000		36,000		6,000 A
		81,000		90,000	
Total costs		165,000		167,520	2,520 A

Before answering the managing director's queries, you investigate the power cost and find out that, although not variable with output, the quarterly cost does vary because it is affected by the outside temperature. You find that the seasonal variations for the cost of power are on average:

Quarter 1	Quarter 2	Quarter 3	Quarter 4
+5%	-10%	-20%	+25%

Required:

Write a report to the managing director, answering his queries. Include cost reports for the year and for the quarter in a form that gives more useful information, explaining briefly the changes you have made.

11.8 It is 1 March and Professor Pauline Heath has just taken up her new appointment as the Head of the Postgraduate Business Studies Department in a new university. Due to unfilled vacancies throughout the current academic year, the department has had to rely on part-time academic staff. The cost of part-time staff who are self-employed is coded to account number 321, while those who are taxed under the Pay-As-You-Earn system are charged to account code 002. Both types of staff enter their claims within ten days of each month-end and these then appear in the management reports of the subsequent month. There are also unfilled clerical and administrative staff vacancies.

The university has a residential conference centre, which the department makes use of from time to time. Sometimes this is because the department's allocated rooms are all in use and sometimes because the department teaches at weekends. The charge for the use of the centre is coded to account 673. An alternative to using the conference centre is to hire outside facilities at local hotels, in which case the expenditure is coded to account 341.

The main forms of income are tuition fees and a higher education grant from the government. The extent of this grant is known before the commencement of the academic year and is payable in two parts, one-third at the end of December and the balance at the end of April.

One of Professor Heath's first tasks was to check the enrolments for the current year. The financial and academic year commenced on 1 September and is subdivided into three terms, each lasting four months. The Autumn term commenced on 1 September and the Spring term on 1 January. All courses commence at the beginning of the Autumn term, the MBA and MSc courses lasting three terms and the diploma course two terms.

The departmental administrator has presented Professor Heath with the enrolment data for the current academic year. Whilst absorbing this information, she has also received the latest management accounts for the department. Both sets of information are reproduced below and on the next page.

Professor Heath is experiencing difficulties in understanding the latest management report. She has written a memo to the university's finance director expressing her anxieties about the presentation of the report and its detailed contents.

Enrolment data-current academic year	*Fee (£)*	*Enrolments*	*Income (£)*
MBA – three terms	3,500	160	560,000
MSc – three terms	3,200	80	256,000
Diploma Course – two terms	1,200	100	120,000
			936,000

Required:

(a) (i) Rearrange the account headings into a more meaningful form for managers. This should include columnar headings for any financial data you feel is appropriate but you do not need to include any figures.

(ii) Briefly justify your proposals.

(b) In her memo, Professor Heath states that the current form of report does not help her manage her department. Identify the strengths and weaknesses apparent in the current system, other than the presentational ones covered in (a), and make and justify outline proposals that will help her manage the department.

(c) Referring to the detailed financial data under the heading of Income, reproduce the actual income to date in a form consistent with accounting principles.

Department of Postgraduate Business Studies
Monthly Management Report – February

Code	Account heading	Annual budget	6 months to 28 February Actual	6 months to 28 February Budget	Variance	Budget remaining
	Expenses					
001	Full-time academic	600,000	230,000	300,000	70,000	370,000
002	Part-time academic	84,000	48,000	42,000	–6,000	36,000
003	Clerical and administration	84,000	36,000	42,000	6,000	48,000
218	Teaching and learning material	30,000	0	15,000	15,000	30,000
321	Teaching and research fees	20,000	19,000	10,000	–9,000	1,000
331	Agency staff (clerical and administrative)	300	2,400	150	–2,250	–2,100
341	External room hire	1,000	400	500	100	600
434	Course advertising (press)	26,000	600	13,000	12,400	25,400
455	Postage and telephone recharge	8,000	1,200	4,000	2,800	6,800
673	Internal room hire	24,000	14,000	12,000	–2,000	10,000
679	Central services recharge	340,000	170,000	170,000	0	170,000
680	Rental light and heat recharge	260,000	130,000	130,000	0	130,000
		1,477,300	651,600	738,650	87,050	825,700
	Income					
802	Tuition fees	900,000	936,000	900,000	–36,000	–36,000
890	Higher education grant	750,000	250,000	250,000	0	500,000
		1,650,000	1,186,000	1,150,000	–36,000	464,000
	Net surplus/deficit	172,700	534,400	411,350	–123,050	–361,700

Assignments

This section contains eighteen assignments.

These comprise sets of extended activities, often based on more than one chapter, which consolidate learning and prepare the student for assessment for Units 8 & 9.

Details of the assignments and chapter coverage are set out on the next two pages.

INTRODUCTION TO ASSIGNMENTS

These Assignments are designed to be used for practice as you progress through the *Managing Performance & Resources Tutorial* text. It is important to be able to apply the appropriate methods and techniques that you have learned to whatever Case Study scenario you may be given.

These Assignments therefore provide a variety of situations. They are linked to specific chapters of the tutorial. The list opposite shows the relevant chapters which should be studied before attempting each Assignment.

This section is not intended to give complete coverage of both units on its own. Further practice of the application of other methods can be gained by using the Workbook Activities for each chapter and the practice Examinations.

HFD PLC – ABSORPTION AND MARGINAL COSTING

1

Relevant Tutorial chapter: 1

SITUATION

HFD plc plans to open a new division on 1 December 2004. The division, HFD Processes Ltd, will produce a special paint finish and the production process is such that there is never any work-in-progress. The original operating budget, shown below, was prepared on the basis that there would be a loss in the initial year of operation and there would be no closing stock of finished goods.

HFD Processes Ltd – budget for the year ended 30 November 2005

Production volume: 20,000 units

	£000s	*£000s*
Turnover (20,000 units)		960
Direct costs		
Material	240	
Production labour	260	
Light, heat and power	68	
Total direct costs	568	
Fixed overheads	400	
Cost of sales		968
Operating profit/(loss)		(8)

Notes:

- Because of the technology involved, production employees are paid per week, irrespective of production levels. In other words, production labour is a fixed cost. (The employees assumed in the budget are capable of producing up to 26,000 units.)
- The cost of material varies directly with production (a variable cost).
- The cost of light, heat and power includes a fixed standing charge and an amount per unit. In the budget, the fixed charge was calculated as £20,000 per year and the variable part as £2.40 per unit of output.

The manager of the new division reviewed this budget and considered the forecast sales volume to be optimistic and that the budget should allow for some closing stock. He suggests that a forecast of 17,000 units of sales would be more appropriate, with output being at 20,000 units, leaving 3,000 units in closing stock.

TASKS

1 State whether the recorded profit figure in the original budget would be the same using marginal costing as with absorption costing, giving your reason.

2 Calculate the following for the paint finish produced by HFD Processes Ltd:

(a) the budgeted unit selling price

(b) the budgeted material cost per unit

(c) the total variable cost per unit

(d) the total cost per unit if all fixed costs are absorbed on a per unit basis, based on production of 20,000 units

3 Present a revised budget statement for the year ended 30 November 2005, with output of 20,000 units but only 17,000 units sold, in line with the manager's suggestion, as follows:

(a) using absorption costing, with all fixed costs absorbed on a per unit basis, based on the budgeted output of 20,000 units

(b) using marginal costing

(c) showing the reason for the difference in recorded profit/loss between your two versions (a) and (b)

4 An executive of the parent company HFD plc assures the divisional manager that he is being too pessimistic and suggests a further budget be prepared. Using marginal costing, calculate the budgeted profit/loss that would be obtained by HFD Processes Ltd for the year ended 30 November 2005 if 25,000 units were made and 22,000 were sold.

5 Comment briefly on whether the method of marginal or absorption costing is to be preferred for preparing budgets for HFD Processes Ltd.

MEDPAK LIMITED – ACTIVITY BASED COSTING

2

Relevant Tutorial chapter: 1

SITUATION

Medpak Ltd is a business which packages pills into the blister packs which are issued to patients.

The pills are received in various sizes of bulk packs from the drug manufacturers. At Medpak Ltd they are then checked and coded according to the type of drug, the size of blister packs needed and other special instructions.

The machine which inserts the pills into the blister packs must be maintained in a controlled environment, and cleaned and set up for each type of drug and size of pack.

The packs are then checked, packed in boxes of 100, coded and dispatched back to the drug manufacturers for onward distribution to customers.

Just before dispatch, a sample of 1 in every 20 boxes is taken for inspection to ensure that control and quality are being maintained throughout the system.

On average, Medpak Ltd receives 2,000 boxes of pills from the manufacturers each year. These require 1,350 packaging runs on the machine, producing 180,000 blister packs. The packs are dispatched in 1,800 boxes of 100 packs.

Medpak Ltd has budgeted overheads of £382,000 per year. Activity based costing is to be introduced in order to include the cost of overheads in the cost of the work being carried out. The coding systems and automated packaging allow all necessary data to be collected on the computer system.

The assistant manager of Medpak Ltd has some accounting knowledge and codes and inputs all financial data. You are employed by a firm of accountants, AMC Services, of whom Medpak Ltd is a client.

TASKS

1 Write a memo to the assistant manager of Medpak Ltd, including the following:

(a) Explain briefly the main principles of activity based costing.

(b) Suggest the four main activities which can be identified in Medpak Ltd as described above.

(c) Suggest suitable cost drivers for each of the four main activities.

(d) Use the following examples to illustrate the allocation of overheads to cost pools:

- the cost of cardboard boxes for dispatch of packs
- the inspector's salary
- depreciation of the blister packaging machine
- delivery and insurance charges on goods sent out
- depreciation of bar code machine for coding drugs received

2 After all the budgeted overheads have been allocated to the four activities, the totals are as shown below. Calculate the cost driver rates to be applied to the work done for the use of each activity.

Use the information relating to budgeted levels of activity given above.

	Budgeted overheads
Receiving goods	£40,000
Blister packaging	£195,750
Dispatch	£126,000
Inspection	£20,250

3 Using activity based costing, calculate the overheads which would be included in the cost of a batch of pills which

- arrived from the manufacturer in two boxes
- required only one run on the packaging machine
- was sent back to the manufacturer in two boxes

HI-LITE – STANDARD COSTING & VARIANCE ANALYSIS

3

Relevant Tutorial chapters: 1,2,3

SITUATION

Hi-Lite is a provider of commercial window-cleaning services for shops and offices.

Standard costing is used in Hi-Lite for each type of service the firm provides, one of which is the cleaning of shop display windows.

The following budgeted and standard costing information relates to the shop window cleaning service.

Budgeted total fixed overheads per year	£24,000
Standard direct labour time per window	10 minutes
Planned number of windows to be cleaned per year	9,600 windows
Cost of direct materials used	£0.15 per window cleaned
Standard direct labour rate	£5.40 per hour

Fixed overheads are to be absorbed on the basis of standard direct labour hours.

It is expected that both the work done and the fixed overheads incurred will be spread evenly over the year.

The cost of direct materials per window has been calculated as the average cost of various cleaning materials used.

The actual results for Hi-Lite for the month of October 2004 were as follows

Actual total overheads for the month	£2,250
Actual number of windows cleaned	744 windows
Actual direct labour hours worked	135 hours
Actual total cost of direct labour	£700
Actual total cost of direct materials	£125

TASKS

For Hi-Lite's shop window cleaning service:

1 Calculate the total standard cost per window cleaned.

2 Calculate the monthly budget for each element of cost (direct material, direct labour and fixed overhead).

3 For the month of October 2004, calculate the following variances:

   (a) Direct material total cost variance
   (b) Direct labour rate variance
   (c) Direct labour efficiency variance
   (d) Fixed overhead expenditure variance
   (e) Fixed overhead capacity variance
   (f) Fixed overhead efficiency variance
   (g) Fixed overhead volume variance

4 Reconcile the total standard cost of the actual work done in October 2004 with the total actual cost, detailing all the variances calculated.

5 Explain why it is not possible in this case to split the direct material variance into price and usage variances.

6 On investigation, it is found that in October 2004 the following factors affected the shop window cleaning service

   - A new employee without previous experience in window-cleaning started work with Hi-Lite.
   - A shop which was one of Hi-Lite's regular customers closed down during October.
   - Two more shops which used Hi-Lite's service announced they would be closing in the near future.
   - During October Hi-Lite commenced an advertising campaign to obtain new customers to replace those lost and likely to be lost through closures.

   For each of these factors, state which of the variances calculated in 3 above would be likely to be affected and explain briefly whether the effect would be adverse or favourable.

SURE PLC – CALCULATION & INTERPRETATION OF VARIANCES

Relevant Tutorial chapters: 1,2,3,4

SITUATION

Sure plc is a manufacturer of fire-proof containers for documents, disks and other data storage media.

You are employed as a Cost Accountant by Sure plc.

The following data relate to one of Sure plc's products, a document box. Sure plc uses standard costing, and variances are calculated on a monthly basis. Variances and subvariances which exceed plus or minus 5% of budget are considered significant and are investigated.

The production of the document boxes is semi-automated and Sure plc uses absorption costing and bases the absorption of fixed overheads on machine hours.

There are two grades of labour for this product:

- Grade I employees prepare the materials and operate the machinery
- Grade II employees check and finish the products

The standard cost per unit of the document box is detailed below, together with the variance report for September 2003 and the actual results for the month of October 2003.

Sure plc fire-proof document box			
Standard Cost per unit	*Quantity*	*Unit cost*	*Total*
Direct material	0.5 kg	£8.20	£4.10
Direct labour Grade I	0.25 hours	£4.60	£1.15
Direct Labour Grade II	0.5 hours	£5.50	£2.75
Fixed overhead	0.6 hours*	£20.00	£12.00
Total			£20.00

* Note that fixed overhead is absorbed on machine hours, which are set at 0.6 hours per unit and the absorption rate is £20.00 per machine hour.

The fixed overhead absorption rate has been calculated on the basis of production of 1,200 boxes per month, and therefore budgeted machine hours are 720 per month and total budgeted fixed overheads are £14,400 per month.

Sure plc: fire-proof document box

Variance report September 2003: output = 1,000 units

	£	£
Standard cost of 1,000 units		20,000
Variances		
Direct material (actual usage 485 kg)		
Price (Adverse)	97	
Usage (Favourable)	(123)	
Grade I Direct Labour		
Rate	–	
Efficiency (Favourable)	(23)	
Grade II Labour		
Rate (Adverse)	77	
Efficiency (Adverse)	275	
Fixed overheads		
Expenditure (Adverse)	200	
Capacity (Adverse)	1,600	
Efficiency (Adverse)	800	2,903
Actual cost of 1,000 units		22,903

Investigation of the significant variances has shown that there was a problem with one of the machines during September, resulting in additional maintenance being required and causing extra work on some of the units for the Grade II employees.

Sure plc: fire-proof document box

Actual results for October 2003: 1,100 units produced

Direct material	530 kg used	cost £4,452
Grade I Direct labour	270 hours	cost £1,250
Grade II Direct labour	600 hours	cost £3,384
Machine hours used	660 hours	
Actual fixed overheads		£14,750

TASKS

1 Calculate all the variances for the fire-proof document box and prepare the variance report for October 2003 in the same format as that given for September 2003.

2 With reference to the information given for Sure plc, explain briefly the term 'control limits' in relation to the investigation of the causes for variances.

3 Sure plc set the standard price of the direct material when a specific price index for the material was expected to remain at 109 throughout the year 2003. However, the index actually rose to 111 by September 2003.

For each of the months September and October 2003, calculate the part of the direct material price variance due to the actual change in the price index and the part due to other influences.

4 Using information from the Case Study to illustrate your answer, write a memo to the Financial Manager of Sure plc explaining why it is important to analyse trends in the monthly variances in addition to preparing the separate monthly reports.

BELLA HOLIDAYS CAR HIRE – VARIANCES DUE TO EXCHANGE RATE CHANGES

5

Relevant Tutorial chapters: 1,2,3,4

SITUATION

Bella Holidays is a UK travel agent, specialising in holidays on Ay Island, where the unit of currency is the Ay Mark (AM).

Bella Holidays sells one type of standard car hire package to its customers as an optional extra on their holiday. Bella Holidays purchases bookings for these contracts from AyCars, the owners of a fleet of hire cars on the island. Bella Holidays published the price to be charged to their customers for the car hire package throughout the season as £300, which represented a 20% mark-up on the standard cost. It was based on a standard cost of £250 or AM275, assuming that the exchange rate would average £1 = AM1.10. The exchange rate given for each month in the table below is the relevant rate for the payment of that month's invoice from AyCars. You have the following information relating to the four month period from March to June 2003 inclusive:

2003	*March*	*April*	*May*	*June*
Number of car hire contracts	20	18	24	21
Exchange Rate: £1 =	AM1.09	AM1.11	AM1.05	AM1.09
AyCars Invoice (AM)	5,100	4,896	6,696	6,006

TASKS

Prepare a report for your manager, Ann Miles, in the Accounts Department of Bella Holidays. The report should incorporate the three tasks shown below.

1 Set out the following information in tabulated format for the each of the four months March to June 2003 inclusive:

(a) the total cost in £ (to the nearest £1) to Bella Holidays of the car hire contracts, using the exchange rates given

(b) the total standard cost for the given number of contracts, using the standard as £250 per contract

(c) the equivalent in £ (to the nearest penny) of the standard cost, AM275, using the exchange rates given

(d) the total standard cost in £ (to the nearest £1) for the given number of contracts, using the figures calculated in (c) above

(e) the total price variance in £ for car hire,

(f) the part of the price variance in £ which is due to variations in the exchange rate,

(g) the part of the price variance in £ which is due to differences in the price charged by AyCars.

2 Assuming that you are given the average actual cost in AM per car hire contract for each of the months November 2002 to June 2003 inclusive, as shown in the table below, identify the underlying trend in the average actual cost, for this period, by calculating *three-point moving averages.*

Average actual cost per car hire contract:

Month	*Average Actual cost Per car-hire contract (AM)*
2002	
November	240
December	245
2003	
January	245
February	250
March	255
April	272
May	279
June	286

3 Comment on the results of your analysis in 1 and 2 above, in particular:

(a) the usefulness of the analysis of the price variances into two parts

(b) any identifiable trends which can be seen in the variances, without further calculations

(c) for each of the variances calculated in Task 1 (f) and (g), an indication of the area of responsibility of the person to whom the variances should be reported and **one** suggestion as to the control action which could be taken by Bella Holidays management in relation to the variances calculated in Task 1 (g)

(d) the usefulness of the moving average trend calculated for the average actual cost in AM for car hire contracts and your comments on this trend

NGJ LTD - VARIANCE ANALYSIS AND ACTIVITY BASED COSTING

Relevant Tutorial chapters: 1,2,3,4

6

SITUATION

NGJ Ltd is a furniture manufacturer. It makes 3 products, the Basic, the Grand and the Super. You are the management accountant reporting to the product line manager for the Basic. Reproduced below is NGJ's unit standard material and labour cost data and budgeted production for the year to 31 May 2003 together with details of the budgeted and actual factory fixed overheads for the year.

Unit standard material and labour cost data by product for the year to 31 May 2003.

Product	*Basic*	*Grand*	*Super*
Material at £12 per metre	6 metres	8 metres	10 metres
Labour at £5.00 per hour	6 hours	1 hour	1 hour
Budgeted production	10,000 units	70,000 units	70,000 units

Total budgeted and actual factory fixed overheads for the year to 31 May 2003

	Budgeted	*Actual*
	£	£
Rent and rates	£100,000	£100,000
Depreciation	£200,000	£200,000
Light, heat and power	£60,000	£70,000
Indirect labour	£240,000	£260,000
Total factory fixed overheads	£600,000	£630,000

Apportionment policy:

As all products are made in the same factory, budgeted and actual total factory fixed overheads are apportioned to each product on the basis of budgeted total labour hours per product.

Basics: actual results

During the year 11,500 Basics were made. The actual amount of material used, labour hours worked and costs incurred were as follows:

Actual material and labour cost of producing 11,500 Basics for the year to 31 May 2003

	Units	*Total cost*
Material	69,230 metres	£872,298
Labour	70,150 hours	£343,735

TASKS

1 (a) Calculate the following information:

(i) the total budgeted labour hours of production for NGJ Ltd;

(ii) the standard factory fixed overhead rate per labour hour;

(iii) the budgeted and actual factory fixed overhead apportioned to Basic production;

(iv) the actual cost of material per metre and the actual labour hourly rate for Basic production;

(v) the total standard absorption cost of actual Basic production;

(vi) the actual absorption cost of actual Basic production.

(b) Calculate the following variances for Basic production:

(i) the material price variance;

(ii) the material usage variance;

(iii) the labour rate variance;

(iv) the labour efficiency variance;

(v) the fixed overhead expenditure variance;

(vi) the fixed overhead volume variance;

(vii) the fixed overhead capacity variance;

(viii) the fixed overhead efficiency variance.

(c) Prepare a statement reconciling the actual absorption cost of actual Basic production with the standard absorption cost of actual Basic production.

2 The product line manager for the Basic is of the opinion that the standard costs and variances do not fairly reflect the effort put in by staff. The manager made the following points:

- because of a shortage of materials for the Basic, the purchasing manager had entered into a contract for the year with a single supplier in order to guarantee supplies;
- the actual price paid for the material per metre was 10% less than the market price throughout the year;
- the Basic is a hand-made product made in a small, separate part of the factory and uses none of the expensive machines shared by the Grand and the Super;
- Grand and Super production uses the same highly mechanised manufacturing facilities and only one of those products can be made at any one time. A change in production from one product to another involves halting production in order to set up the necessary tools and production line.

In response to a request from the Basic product line manager, a colleague has re-analysed the budgeted and actual factory fixed overheads by function. The revised analysis is reproduced below:

Functional analysis of factory fixed overheads for the year ended 31 May 2003

	Budget	*Actual*
	£	£
Setting up of tools and production lines	202,000	228,000
Depreciation attributable to production	170,000	170,000
Stores	60,000	59,000
Maintenance	40,000	48,000
Light, heat and power directly attributable to production	48,000	45,000
Rent and rates directly attributable to production	80,000	80,000
Total factory fixed overheads	600,000	630,000

Write a memo to the Basic product line manager. Your memo should:

(a) identify the market price of the material used in the Basic;

(b) subdivide the material price variance into that part due to the contracted price being different from the market price and that due to other reasons;

(c) identify ONE benefit to NGJ Ltd, which is not reflected in the variances, arising from the purchasing manager's decision to enter into a contract for the supply of materials;

(d) briefly explain what is meant by activity-based costing;

(e) refer to the task data, where appropriate, to briefly discuss whether or not activity based costing would have reduced the budgeted and actual fixed overheads of Basic production.

COVE PLC – RATIO ANALYSIS

7

Relevant Tutorial chapters: 1,5,6

SITUATION

Cove plc is a chain of retail shops selling sports goods.

Cove plc's main competitor is Bay plc, a larger chain selling similar goods.

As a trainee management accountant in Cove plc, you are asked to analyse the published financial accounts of Bay plc and compare the performance of the two companies for the year ended 30 November 2003.

The following data has been extracted from the financial accounts of the two companies for the year ended 30 November 2003.

Summary Trading and Profit and Loss Accounts for the year ended 30 November 2003

	Cove plc	*Bay plc*
	£000s	*£000s*
Turnover	18,000	22,000
Cost of sales	13,500	15,800
Gross profit	4,500	6,200
Administration	2,950	3,800
Operating Profit (Profit before interest and tax)	1,550	2,400

Summary Balance Sheets as at 30 November 2003

	Cove plc	*Bay plc*
	£000s	*£000s*
Fixed Assets (note 1)	3,456	4,216
Net current assets (note 2)	1,125	1,500
Total assets	4,581	5,716
Long-term loans	-	1,000
	4,581	4,716
Financed by:		
Shareholders' Funds (Capital)	4,581	4,716
	4,581	4,716

Notes:

1 Fixed assets

	Cove plc			**Bay plc**		
	At Cost	*Accum. Deprec.*	*NBV*	*At Cost*	*Accum. Deprec.*	*NBV*
	£000s	*£000s*	*£000s*	*£000s*	*£000s*	*£000s*
Land and Buildings	4,000	960	3,040	9,600	5,760	3,840
Fixtures and Fittings	720	408	312	620	328	292
Vehicles	240	136	104	420	336	84
Total	4,960	1,504	3,456	10,640	6,424	4,216

Straight-line depreciation is used in both companies.

2 Net current assets

	Cove plc	*Bay plc*
	£000s	*£000s*
Stock as at 30 November 2003	1,100	1,700
Debtors	500	680
Cash at Bank and in hand	975	320
	2,575	2,700
Current liabilities	1,450	1,200
Net current assets	1,125	1,500

Average number of employees during the year ended 30 November 2003

Cove plc 140 employees

Bay plc 168 employees

Performance indicators

The following performance indicators have already been calculated for Cove plc for the year ended 30 November 2003:

	Cove plc
Return on capital employed (ROCE)	33.8%
Gross Profit Margin	25.0%
Operating Profit Margin	8.6%
Asset Turnover	3.9 times
Turnover per employee	£128,571
Operating profit per employee	£11,071
Current Ratio	1.8 : 1
Acid Test Ratio	1.0 : 1
Average age of closing stock	30 days

TASKS

1 Calculate the nine performance indicators listed above for Bay plc for the year ended 30 November 2003.

2 Write a report for the management of Cove plc, in which the following are included:

(a) A table presenting the nine performance indicators listed above for both companies for comparison.

(b) Your comments on the relative performance of the two companies in the year ended 30 November 2003, referring to the original data and the performance indicators.

(c) A brief explanation of the limitations of this analysis of the results of the two companies.

WS POTTERIES LTD – CONTROL RATIOS & QUALITY MANAGEMENT

8

Relevant Tutorial chapters: 1,5,6,7

SITUATION

WS Potteries Ltd is a company which manufactures pottery mugs and plates.

The mugs and plates are produced in two grades: standard and premium. The standard items are produced in large batches and are decorated by a mechanised process using transfers.

The premium items are moulded by machine in the same way as the standard items, but are decorated by hand painting and higher quality materials are used throughout. Hand painting enables WS Potteries Ltd to take orders for individually personalised items in this range, in addition to designs which are used regularly.

Direct costs are higher for the Premium range. This is due to the use of higher quality materials and the skilled labour for hand decoration. The individually personalised items in the Premium range have the highest direct costs per unit, because the hand decoration takes more time for these items.

You are employed in the accounts department of WS Potteries Ltd and have been asked to:

- analyse the following data, relating to weekly production for a period of 4 weeks,
- comment on measures of performance and suggestions for improvements

WEEK:	*1*	*2*	*3*	*4*
Total production (units)	10,916	10,700	11,250	11,200
Machine operators:				
Number of operators	10	10	10	10
Hours paid	400	400	400	400
Productive hours	368	355	375	375
Hand decorators:				
Number of decorators	3	3	4	4
Hours paid	120	120	160	170
Productive hours	105	100	140	148
Units decorated	1,008	985	1,400	1,350

Note: 'Units decorated' includes all Premium items, some of which are individually personalised to order.

You have ascertained that the Week 3 above represents exactly the standard (budgeted) levels of activity, capacity and efficiency and that all workers are paid on the basis of a 40-hour week.

The expected split of the production of 11,250 units per week between the different types of product is as follows:

	Mugs	*Plates*	*Total*
Standard Grade	8,000	1,850	9,850
Premium Grade	1,000	400	1,400
Total	9,000	2,250	11,250

These figures are based on averages, however, as special orders may alter the production scheduling in any given week.

Your investigations have revealed that a new hand decorator commenced work at WS Potteries Ltd in Week 3, and that a number of special orders for personalised Premium plates had to be completed by the end of Week 4.

You have also been told that the numbers of units produced and the numbers of units decorated, given above, represent units which have passed inspections at the end of each process. These quantities do not include units which have been broken or damaged during production or rejected as substandard. Quantities of rejects are not recorded.

WS Potteries Ltd treats the cost of packaging of the products as a direct cost. More expensive packaging materials are used for the Premium grade mugs and plates and specially printed boxes are used for the individually personalised items. The cost of packaging materials used for the units produced in the given period has been analysed as follows, to the nearest £1:

WEEK:	*1*	*2*	*3*	*4*
Total production (units)	10,916	10,700	11,250	11,200
Standard Packaging	£991	£972	£985	£985
Premium Packaging	£200	£195	£224	£275
Printed Boxes	£4	£5	£140	£150

You have investigated the costs of packaging and have found that the costs of packing material for standard items has been maintained at 10p per item, but the cost of materials for packing premium products has increased in Week 4, from 20p to 25p per item. The cost of printed boxes has also increased in Week 4, from 50p to 60p per box.

The increasing cost of packaging has given rise to a discussion between members of the management team, as to whether the same, cheaper packaging materials should be used for all items. The supervisor of the Packing Department argues that this would result in more breakages of Premium products, and that the printed box is an important part of the personalised items.

Opinions which are being put forward centre around the benefits of 'cost reduction', 'value analysis' and 'total quality management'.

TASKS

Prepare a report for the Management Accountant of WS Potteries Ltd, including the following information:

1 (a) Units produced per machine operator in each of the 4 weeks.

(b) The activity (production volume) ratio for the machine operators, based on Week 3 as the standard.

(c) The efficiency ratio for machine operation for each week of the period, using Week 3 as 100%.

(d) Units produced per Hand Decorator in each of the 4 weeks.

(e) The efficiency ratio for hand decoration for each week of the period, using Week 3 as 100%.

(f) Brief comments on the meaning of the activity and efficiency ratios and on the performance of the machine operators and hand decorators in the given period.

2 Include in your report brief explanations of what is meant by the terms 'cost reduction', 'value analysis' and 'total quality management', using the packaging discussion to illustrate your answer.

3 Taking into account ALL the information you have available above, make **two** recommendations in your report as to how the reporting of performance could be improved in WS Potteries Ltd and explain briefly the benefits to the company of your suggested improvements.

TRAVEL BUS LTD - CALCULATING AND DEVELOPING PERFORMANCE INDICATORS

Relevant Tutorial chapters: 1,5,6,7

SITUATION

Travel Bus Ltd is a company owned by Travel Holdings plc. It operates in the town of Camford. Camford is an old town with few parking facilities for motorists. Several years ago, the Town Council built a car park on the edge of the town and awarded Travel Bus the contract to carry motorists and their passengers between the car park and the centre of the town.

Originally, the Council charged motorists £4.00 per day for the use of the car park but, to encourage motorists not to take their cars into the town centre, parking has been free since 1 December 2003.

The journey between the car park and the town centre is the only service operated by Travel Bus Ltd in Camford. A summary of the results for the first two years of operations, together with the net assets associated with the route and other operating data, is reproduced below.

Operating statement year ended 30 November

	2003	2004
	£	£
Turnover	432,000	633,600
Fuel	129,600	185,328
Wages	112,000	142,000
Other variable costs	86,720	84,512
Gross profit	103,680	221,760
Bus road tax and insurance	22,000	24,000
Depreciation of buses	12,000	12,000
Maintenance of buses	32,400	28,512
Fixed garaging costs	29,840	32,140
Administration	42,000	49,076
Net profit (loss)	(34,560)	76,032

Extract from Balance sheet at 30 November

	2003	2004
	£	£
Buses	240,000	240,000
Accumulated depreciation	168,000	180,000
Net book value	72,000	60,000
Net current assets	14,400	35,040
	86,400	95,040

Other operating data	**2003**	**2004**
Fare per passenger per journey	£0.80	£1.00
Miles per year	324,000	356,400
Miles per journey	18.0	18.0
Days per year	360	360
Wages per driver	£14,000	£14,200

Throughout the two years, the drivers were paid a basic wage per week, no bonuses were paid and no overtime was incurred.

In two weeks there will be a meeting between officials of the Town Council and the Chief Executive of Travel Holdings to discuss the performance of Travel Bus for the year to 30 November 2004. The previous year's performance indicators were as follows:

Gross profit margin	24%
Net profit margin	-8%
Return on capital employed	-40%
Asset turnover	5 times
Number of passengers in the year	540,000
Total cost per mile	£1.44
Number of journeys per day	50
Maintenance cost per mile	£0.10
Passengers per day	1,500
Passengers per journey	30
Number of drivers	8

TASKS

1 In preparation for the meeting, you have been asked to calculate the following performance indicators for the year to 30 November 2004.

(a) Gross profit margin;

(b) Net profit margin;

(c) Return on capital employed;

(d) Asset turnover;

(e) Number of passengers in the year

(f) Total cost per mile;

(g) Number of journeys per day;

(h) Maintenance cost per mile;

(i) Passengers per day;

(j) Passengers per journey;

(k) Number of drivers.

2 On receiving your performance indicators, the Chief Executive of Travel Holdings raises the following issues with you:

- the drivers are claiming that the improved profitability of Travel Bus reflects their increased productivity;
- the managers believe that the change in performance is due to improved motivation arising from the introduction of performance related pay for managers during the year to 30 November 2004.
- the officials from the Town Council are concerned that Travel Bus is paying insufficient attention to satisfying passenger needs and safety.

The Chief Executive asks for your advice.

Write a memo to the Chief Executive of Travel Holdings plc. Where relevant, you should make use of the data and answers to Task 1 to:

(a) briefly discuss whether or not increased productivity always leads to increased profitability;

(b) develop ONE possible measure of driver productivity and suggest whether nor not the drivers' claim is valid;

(c) suggest ONE reason, other than improved motivation, why the profitability of Travel Bus might have improved;

(d) suggest:

  (i) ONE existing performance indicator which might measure the satisfaction of passenger needs; and

  (ii) ONE other possible performance indicator of passenger needs which cannot be measured from the existing performance data collected by Travel Bus;

(e) suggest:

  (i) ONE existing performance indicator which might measure the safety aspect of Travel Bus's operations; and

  (ii) ONE other possible safety performance indicator which cannot be measured from the existing performance data collected by Travel Bus.

BON REPOSE HOTELS - PERFORMANCE MEASUREMENT AND SCENARIO PLANNING

Relevant Tutorial chapters: 1,5,6,7

SITUATION

The Bon Repose hotel group is a French company. It builds and operates economy class hotels close to major roads to provide overnight accommodation for motorists. Each bedroom is a standard size and the only food provided for guests is breakfast.

Recently, Bon Repose formed a UK subsidiary and shortly afterwards you were appointed its management accountant. You report to Helene de la Tour, the chief executive of the UK subsidiary who provides you with the following information.

- All Bon Repose hotels have 80 bedrooms and operate for 365 days per year.
- Sales volume is measured in room-nights. Customers are charged for the use of the room per night for either single or double occupancy. A customer staying three nights will, therefore, be charged for three room-nights.
- Creditors relate only to the variable costs incurred by the hotel.
- The company does not provide for depreciation.

The first Bon Repose UK hotel was opened one year ago. Its financial and operating information is shown below.

Operating statement year ended 30 November 2003			Net assets at 30 November 2003		
	£	£		£	£
Turnover		560,640	**Fixed assets**		669,556
Variable costs					
Breakfasts and laundry		175,200			
Contribution		385,440	**Net current assets**		
Fixed costs			Debtors	35,040	
Labour	133,865		Cash	10,804	
Light and heat	89,045			45,844	
Rates, insurance, maintenance	120,482	343,392	Creditors	(14,600)	31,244
Net profit		42,048	**Net assets**		700,800
Actual number of room-nights sold		17,520			

TASKS

1 Helene de la Tour asks you to prepare the following performance indicators for the hotel:

(a) gross (or contribution) margin;

(b) net profit (or sales) margin;

(c) return on capital employed;

(d) asset turnover;

(e) average age of debtors in months;

(f) average age of creditors in months;

(g) the number of months that expenses could be paid from the cash balance;

(h) maximum capacity of the hotel in room-nights;

(i) the percentage room-night occupancy rate of the hotel.

2 On receiving your performance indicators, Helene de la Tour tells you that similar hotels in France are more profitable. She believes one of the reasons for the poor profits at the UK hotel is because the manager has been giving discounts. She tells you of the following company policies.

- The price of each room is £40.00 per night but the manager can reduce this to £20 where necessary.
- The average age of debtors should be 0.5 months.
- The company should take twice as many months to pay its creditors as it currently does.
- The cash balance at the hotel should only be £3,000. Any surplus cash should be transferred to the head office bank account.

You agree to investigate the reasons for the poor profits.

Write a memo to Helene de la Tour. In your memo, you should:

(a) calculate:

(i) what the turnover would have been had there been no discounts;

(ii) the total discount;

(iii) the number of discounted room-nights;

(iv) the percentage of room-nights discounted;

(b) prepare a revised operating statement of net assets assuming that the company's policies had been met but no discounts offered;

(c) calculate the revised:

(i) gross (or contribution) margin;

(ii) net profit (or sales) margin;

(iii) return on capital employed;

(d) briefly discuss whether or not the discounting of prices would have been the reason for the reduced profits.

BELLA HOLIDAYS ACCOMMODATION – SEASONAL VARIATIONS & FORECASTING

11

Relevant Tutorial chapters: 1,8

SITUATION

Note: Assignment 5 is also based on Bella Holidays, but is completely separate. It does not have to be completed before this assignment.

Bella Holidays is a UK travel agent, specialising in holidays on Ay Island, where the unit of currency is the Ay Mark (AM).

The following information relates to the cost per week of a standard twin self-catering apartment in the main resort on Ay Island. Bella Holidays purchases bookings for these apartments from Ay Development Company, the owners of the property on the island.

It has been determined that the average cost per week of a standard twin self-catering apartment is subject to seasonal variations in the four quarters of the year as follows:

	Quarter 1	*Quarter 2*	*Quarter 3*	*Quarter 4*
Variation (Ay Marks)	– 100	– 50	+ 125	+ 25

The average actual cost per week (in Ay Marks) of the apartments has been calculated from the actual amounts charged by Ay Development Company for the last eight quarters as follows:

2002

Quarter 4	AM 212

2003

Quarter 1	AM 150
Quarter 2	AM 265
Quarter 3	AM 502
Quarter 4	AM 470

2004

Quarter 1	AM 404
Quarter 2	AM 520
Quarter 3	AM 760

TASKS

Prepare a report for your manager, Ann Miles, in the Accounts Department of Bella Holidays. The report should incorporate the four tasks shown below.

1 Set out the following information in tabulated format for the period from Quarter 4 of 2002 to Quarter 1 of 2005 inclusive:

(a) the average actual cost per week of a standard twin self-catering apartment in the main resort on Ay Island, for the eight quarters for which this is given,

(b) the given seasonal variation for each quarter

(c) the underlying trend in the average actual cost, for these eight quarters, calculated by 'deseasonalising' the data, that is removing the seasonal variations from the actual figures

(d) forecasts for the trend for the last quarter of 2004 and the first quarter of 2005, using the average change in the trend per quarter

(e) forecasts for the actual cost for the last quarter of 2004 and the first quarter of 2005

2 Draw a graph for the period from Quarter 4 of 2002 to Quarter 1 of 2005 inclusive, showing the information given in the table in 1 above.

3 Comment on the usefulness of the identification of the trend and the forecasting which you have carried out in **1** above.

4 Comment on what further information you require to improve your report for management accounting purposes and how this information would be used.

PRIMECAST LTD – BUDGETING WITH WASTAGE AND GIVEN EFFICIENCY LEVEL

12

Relevant Tutorial chapters: 1,8,9

SITUATION

Primecast Ltd is a manufacturer of cast stone-effect ornamental products for parks and large gardens.

Budgets are prepared for periods of 12 weeks, each week being 5 working days.

The budgeted direct labour rate is £6.00 per hour and the basic working week is 40 hours for full-time employees. Any additional hours are paid at an overtime rate of time and a half, ie £9.00 per hour. There are 13 full-time employees working on production.

In the next 12-week budget period, two products (codes LB1 and SB2) are to be manufactured and the following information is available for preparation of the budget.

Product	*LB1*	*SB2*
Budgeted sales units	2,200	4,500
Direct material in each completed unit	6 kg	2 kg
Direct labour hours per unit	1 hour	0.6 hour

The budgeted cost of direct material is £3.00 per kg. 10% of the material input to the production process is lost and this must be allowed for in the material usage budget.

For the next period, the target efficiency ratio for the productive hours of direct labour is 95%. After budgeting for the required production time, a further 20% of the total production time is to be added, to allow for breaks and for time spent on indirect work such as preparation and cleaning of equipment.

The budgeted opening and closing stock levels for the next 12-week period are as follows:

	Opening stock	*Closing stock*
Direct Material	3,700 kg	4,300 kg
Product LB1 completed units	150 units	800 units
Product SB2 completed units	825 units	600 units

(There are no stocks of work in progress).

TASKS

1 For Primecast Ltd for the next 12-week period, calculate the following:

(a) the production budget in units of each of the two products LB1 and SB2

(b) the total direct material usage budget in kg

(c) the total direct material purchases budget in kg and in £

(d) the standard direct labour hours required for production

(e) the productive hours required at 95% efficiency

(f) the total hours to be budgeted for production workers

(g) the total budgeted cost of production labour including overtime premium

2 Suggest **two** possible ways in which Primecast Ltd could reduce or eliminate the necessity for overtime payments.

PLASTOYS LTD – BUDGETING WITH PRODUCTION SCHEDULING

13

Relevant Tutorial chapters: 1,8,9

SITUATION

Plastoys Ltd is a company which manufactures plastic toys. The toys are produced from different colours of plastic material by automated processes. Plastoys Ltd's sales quantities are affected by seasonal variations. As the toys are moulded by machines, production quantities are limited by the available machine hours.

You are an assistant to the management accountant in Plastoys Ltd and you have been asked to analyse the following data, relating to quarterly production for a period of 2 years, and forecast sales quantities for the following five quarters. The forecast sales can then be used to prepare a production budget for the next year.

QUARTER:	*1*	*2*	*3*	*4*
YEAR 2002				
Total Sales (units)	13,600	20,534	41,400	62,420
YEAR 2003				
Total Sales (units)	13,960	21,076	42,425	64,035

You have ascertained that the seasonal variations in sales quantities of Plastoys Ltd have been found to approximate to the multiplicative (proportional) model, as follows:

QUARTER:	1	2	3	4
Actual units as % of trend	40%	60%	120%	180%

You have also been told that the numbers of units produced per quarter cannot exceed 40,000 units, because of the limited availability of machine hours. It is currently the policy in Plastoys Ltd to produce sufficient units, so that the stock of toys at the end of each quarter is at least 40% of the forecast quantity of Sales for the following quarter.

TASKS

Prepare a report for the Managing Director of Plastoys Ltd, including the following information:

(a) The trend in Sales Quantities (Units), calculated by deseasonalising the actual data for each of the 8 quarters given (years 2002 and 2003).

(b) Forecasts of the trend in Sales Quantities for each of the 4 quarters of 2004 and the first quarter of 2005

(c) Forecasts of the actual Sales Quantities for each of the 4 quarters of 2004 and the first quarter of 2005

(d) The minimum number of units required in closing stock, according to current policy, in the last quarter of 2003 and in each of the 4 quarters of 2004.

(e) The draft Production Budget (in units) for the 4 quarters of 2004, without taking into account the limitation on machine hours, but applying the policy on stock levels by using the minimum amounts required, as calculated above.

(f) An adjusted Production Budget (in units) for the 4 quarters of 2004, taking into account the limitation on machine hours and applying the policy on stock levels. (Note that the policy states 'at least' 40%: the level of 40% may be exceeded).

(g) A brief explanation of **one** reservation you may have relating to the budget proposals calculated above for the given period.

(h) Taking into account all the information you have available above, suggest one way in which the profitability of Plastoys Ltd could be improved without increasing the machine hours available. Explain briefly the financial and the non-financial benefits to the company which would result from your proposal.

ALINE PLC – BUDGETING WITH A LIMITED RESOURCE

14

Relevant Tutorial chapters: 1,8,9

SITUATION

Aline plc currently manufactures two products, Alpha and Beta, using the same direct material and the same direct labour force. The forecast demand for each of these products is 4,000 units per quarter. The direct material costs £5 per kg and the direct labour rate is £7 per hour. The following budgeted data relates to the two products:

	Alpha	*Beta*
Selling price per unit	£35	£40
Direct material per unit	1.8 kg	2.0 kg
Direct labour per unit	1.5 hours	1.5 hours

The company requires the stocks at the end of each quarter to be:

Direct material:	3,200 kg
Alpha:	1,000 units
Beta:	1,000 units

There are no stocks of work-in-progress.

In the next quarter, Aline plc is to launch a third product, Gamma, which uses the same direct material and direct labour force as Alpha and Beta. Each unit of Gamma uses 3.2 kg of direct material and takes 0.75 hours of direct labour. The selling price of Gamma will be £45 per unit. As this is a new product, there are no opening stocks of finished units. The demand for Gamma in its first quarter is expected to be 3,000 units and the managers of Aline plc would like to build up a closing stock of 1,000 units of Gamma.

For all three products, direct material and direct labour are the only variable costs. There will be no additional fixed costs incurred for the product Gamma.

TASKS

1 Calculate the total amount of direct material required to produce 4,000 units of each of the products Alpha and Beta.

2 For each of the products Alpha and Beta, calculate the following:

(a) the variable cost per product unit

(b) the contribution per product unit

3 Calculate the total contribution that Aline plc would obtain from sales of 4,000 units of each of the products Alpha and Beta.

4 For the product Gamma, calculate:

(a) the variable cost per unit

(b) the contribution per product unit

(c) the total amount of direct material required for production in the first quarter, assuming the managers' stock policy is applied.

5 The managers of Aline plc are informed by their supplier that the direct material used in Alpha, Beta and Gamma will be temporarily in short supply and Aline plc will be able to purchase only 20,000 kg in the next quarter. The sales manager suggests that equal quantities of Alpha, Beta and Gamma should be produced and sold. The finance director wants to produce the quantities that will maximise the company's profit. Calculate, for the next quarter:

(a) the number of units of each product that could be produced if the usual level of direct material stock is maintained and if the sales manager's idea is applied

(b) the total contribution that would result from the planned production in (a), assuming that production and sales quantities are equal

(c) the number of units of each of the products Alpha, Beta and Gamma that should be produced in order to maximise profit, assuming that the usual level of direct material stock is maintained

(d) the total contribution that would result from the planned production in (c), assuming that production and sales quantities are equal

6 Comment briefly on:

(a) the advantages and disadvantages of the sales manager's and the finance director's ideas

(b) **one** way in which Aline plc could improve profits still further in the next quarter.

MOTOSTAY MOTELS LTD – BUDGETING IN A SERVICE ORGANISATION

15

Relevant Tutorial chapters: 1,8,9,10

SITUATION

Motostay Motels Ltd is a company which owns and runs motels situated on motorways and major routes around the UK.

All the motels have one type of room, with exactly the same standard of facilities. The accommodation is priced at £50 per room per night throughout all the motels and is not dependent on the number of people occupying the room or the time of year. The motels remain open all the year round (365 days).

Motostay Motels Ltd has a central office which houses a computerised booking and accounting system which is linked up to all the motels where the bookings are taken.

The external maintenance of the buildings is also centralised, but day-to-day repairs and internal maintenance are the responsibility of each motel manager. This work is normally sub-contracted to local businesses, on an annual service charge basis. The individual motels do not employ maintenance staff.

Cleaning staff are employed by each motel manager and are paid on an hourly basis. Administrative staff are also employed, to take bookings, work on reception, deal with guests' payments and input data to the computer system. Staff must be available for this work every day from 6 am until midnight. The manager of the motel normally covers part of this work.

The standards set by Motostay Motels Ltd for customer service are applied in all the motels. Every occupied room is thoroughly cleaned every day and all bedlinen and towels replaced, whether or not there is a change of guests. The rooms contain consumables for the tea and coffee making facilities and also for the bathrooms. For costing purposes it is assumed that these are all replaced every day in each room which is occupied. Rooms which are unoccupied are kept clean, but this takes the cleaners less time than for the occupied rooms, and the laundry and consumables costs are not incurred.

Other costs incurred include fees for TV channels, which are not dependent on whether the rooms are occupied or not, and electricity, which is reduced when the rooms are unoccupied.

You are a trainee manager with Motostay Motels Ltd and have been given the following information about a particular motel, reference number M215, which contains 80 rooms. The cost unit for cost accounting purposes is the room-night, ie one room for one night. From the information given above, it can be seen that certain costs per room-night will differ between occupied and unoccupied rooms.

During the year to 31 March 2003, the level of occupancy at the motel was 52%. (Level of occupancy is the number of occupied room-nights as a percentage of the total available room-nights.)

During the year ended 31 March 2003, the following unit costs have been incurred in Motel M215:

	Occupied Room-night	*Unoccupied Room-night*
	£	£
Laundry	7.50	–
Cleaning (wages)	4.80	0.60
Cleaning (materials)	0.20	0.10
Consumables	3.25	–
Electricity	3.85	1.65
TV channel fees (£)	0.95	0.95

Other Fixed Costs:

Salaries (manager and administration staff)	£135,000 for the year.
Contracts for internal maintenance	£55,000 for the year.

Some changes in the above costs are anticipated for the year commencing 1 April 2003, as follows:

Laundry charges to increase by 2%

Cleaning wages to increase by 5%

Consumables to increase by 4%

All fixed costs to increase by 5%

TASKS

As part of your training course, you are required to set out your answers to the following in the form of a report to the Management Accountant of Motostay Motels Ltd.

1 For Motel M215, for the year ended 31 March 2003:

- Calculate the total available room-nights for the year.
- Calculate the number of occupied room-nights, given the level of occupancy as 52%.
- Calculate the corresponding number of unoccupied room-nights.
- Calculate the total costs for the motel for the year.
- Calculate the total sales revenue for the motel for the year, assuming all sales were at £50 per room per night.
- Calculate the profit for the motel for the year.

2 For Motel M215 for the year from 1 April 2003 to 31 March 2004, assuming the anticipated cost increases occur:

- Calculate the revised unit costs for an occupied room-night and an unoccupied room-night.
- Calculate the total costs at a level of occupancy of 60%.
- Calculate the total costs at a level of occupancy of 80%.
- Calculate the profit for the motel for the year at each of these two levels of occupancy, assuming all sales are at £50 per room per night.
- Calculate the profit for the motel for the year, if the 80% level of occupancy was achieved by introducing a special offer. This offer would mean that all extra sales above the 60% level were at half price.

3 Comment on the results of your calculations in 1 and 2 above. Also explain briefly two important considerations to be taken into account by Motostay Motels Ltd, when determining whether to introduce special offers to boost sales.

LUKE PLC – BUDGETING USING MARGINAL COSTING

16

Relevant Tutorial chapters: 1,8,9,10,11

SITUATION

You are the Management Accountant of Luke plc, a company which manufactures a single product.

The budget for Luke plc for the year ended 31 July 2003 was originally prepared on the basis of production and sales of 40,000 product units.

The Chief Executive of Luke plc did not consider that the budgeted profit would meet company targets, and imposed a budget based on a reduction of the selling price and a higher sales volume. In order to improve the profit, there was also a requirement to increase productivity and to cut fixed administration costs.

The original and revised budgets are given below. Production labour is treated as a fixed cost and the revised budget does not allow for any increase. The additional production is to be achieved by improvements in productivity. Power is a semi-variable cost. 'Other fixed costs' include Administration Costs, which the Chief Executive expects to be reduced by £100,000 for the year.

The actual results for Luke plc for the year ended 31 July 2003 are also given. The Chief Executive was concerned that the actual net profit was lower than that shown in the original budget.

Production reached the revised volume of 46,000 units, but sales volume was 42,000 units, therefore closing stock of finished goods was 4,000 units. (There were no opening stocks of finished goods and no opening or closing work-in-progress).

Luke plc: Budgets for the year to 31 July 2003

	Original Budget		**Revised Budget**	
Production and Sales	40,000 units		46,000 units	
	£000s	*£000s*	*£000s*	*£000s*
Turnover		2,000.0		2,070.0
Less: Production Cost of Sales				
Direct Materials	360.0		414.0	
Production Labour	289.0		289.0	
Power	90.0	739.0	102.0	805.0
Gross Profit		1,261.0		1,265.0
Less:				
Other Fixed Costs		850.0		750.0
Net Profit		411.0		515.0

Luke plc: Actual results for the year to 31 July 2003

	£000s	£000s
Turnover (42,000 units sold)		1,890.0
Less: Cost of Sales		
Opening Stock	–	
Production cost of 46,000 units		
Direct Materials	409.4	
Production Labour	295.6	
Power	77.0	
	782.0	
Less Closing Stock (4,000 units)	(68.0)	714.0
Gross Profit		1,176.0
Less:		
Other Fixed Costs		788.0
Net Profit		388.0

TASKS

1 Calculate, for Luke plc for the year to 31 July 2003:

- the original budgeted selling price per product unit
- the revised budgeted selling price per product unit
- the budgeted direct material cost per product unit
- the fixed and variable parts of the budgeted cost of power
- the actual variable cost of power, given that the actual fixed part of the cost was £2,000 less than the budget

2 Using marginal costing, prepare a performance statement for Luke plc for the year to 31 July 2003 showing

- a flexed budget for sales of 42,000 units and production of 46,000 units, based on the revised budget (Closing stock is to be valued at budgeted variable cost.)
- the actual results set out in marginal costing format, with closing stocks valued at actual variable cost
- the variances for turnover and each element of cost

3 Write a report to the Chief Executive of Luke plc

- explaining briefly the conditions under which it is likely that employees will be motivated to work towards an imposed budget
- commenting on any indications in the actual results, shown in your performance statement for the year to 31 July 2003, as to whether the employees were motivated by the imposed budget
- stating the two main reasons why the actual profit for the year to 31 July 2003 was less than the profit shown in the imposed revised budget
- stating the main reason why the actual profit for the year to 31 July 2003 was less than the profit shown in the original budget

RIVERMEDE LTD – FLEXIBLE BUDGETING AND PARTICIPATION IN BUDGETING

Relevant Tutorial chapters: 1,8,9,10,11

SITUATION

Rivermede Ltd makes a single product called the Fasta. Last year, Steven Jones, the managing director of Rivermede Ltd, attended a course on budgetary control. As a result, he agreed to revise the way budgets were prepared in the company. Rather than imposing targets for managers, he encouraged participation by senior managers in the preparation of budgets.

An initial budget was prepared but Mike Fisher, the sales director, considered that the budgeted sales volume was set too high. He explained that setting too high a budgeted sales volume would mean his sales staff would be demotivated because they would not be able to achieve that sales volume. Steven Jones agreed to use the revised sales volume suggested by Mike Fisher.

Both the initial and revised budgets are reproduced below, complete with the actual results for the year ended 31 May 2009.

Rivermede Ltd – budgeted and actual costs for the year ended 31 May 2009

	Original Budget	*Revised Budget*	*Actual Results*	*Variances from revised Budget*
Fasta production & sales (units)	24,000	20,000	22,000	2,000 F
	£	£	£	£
Variable costs				
Material	216,000	180,000	206,800	26,800 A
Labour	288,000	240,000	255,200	15,200 A
Semi-variable costs				
Heat, light and Power	31,000	27,000	33,400	6,400 A
Fixed costs				
Rent, rates & depreciation	40,000	40,000	38,000	2,000 F
	575,000	487,000	533,400	46,400 A

Assumptions in the two budgets

1 No change in input prices.

2 No change in the quantity of variable inputs per Fasta.

As the management accountant at Rivermede Ltd, one of your tasks is to check that invoices have been properly coded. On checking the actual invoices for heat, light and power for the year to 31 May 2009, you find that one invoice for £7,520 had been incorrectly coded. The invoice should have been coded to materials.

TASKS

1 (a) Using the information in the original and revised budgets, identify:

- the variable cost of material and labour per Fasta
- the fixed and unit variable cost within heat, light and power

(b) Prepare a flexible budget performance statement, including variances, for Rivermede Ltd after correcting for the miscoding of the invoice.

2 On reviewing the flexible budget performance report you have prepared in Task 1:

- Mike Fisher, the sales director states that it shows that his participation in revising the sales budget motivated the sales staff to achieve better results.
- Steven Jones, the managing director, is not sure whether the participative approach has been successful, in particular because the effects of the revised budget were not fully investigated before it was implemented. He considers that the use of flexible budgeting and the reporting of results should enable him to improve the planning process as well as the control of the business.

(a) Give **two** reasons why the actual sales may have exceeded the revised budget, other than the reason given by Mike Fisher.

(b) Explain briefly how flexible budgeting and the reporting of results can assist with planning and control through the use of 'feedforward' and 'feedback' of information.

PARKSIDE MANUFACTURING LTD – FLEXIBLE BUDGETING AND FORECASTING

18

Relevant Tutorial chapters: 1,8,9,10,11

SITUATION

You have recently been appointed as the management accountant of Parkside Manufacturing Ltd. Parkside Manufacturing makes a single product, the Delta. The previous management accountant has already prepared an analysis of budgeted and actual results for the year to 30 November 2003. These are reproduced below:

Parkside Manufacturing Ltd

Operating Statement for year ended 30 November 2003

Volume (number of Deltas)	**Budget** *100,000*		**Actual** *125,000*		**Variance**
	£000	*£000*	*£000*	*£000*	*£000*
Turnover		2,000		2,250	250 (F)
Material	600		800		200 (A)
Light, heat and power	200		265		65 (A)
Production labour	120		156		36 (A)
Rent, rates and depreciation	140		175		35 (A)
Administrative expenses	110		110		nil
		1,170		1,506	
Profit		830		744	86 (A)
Key: (F) = favourable, (A) = adverse					

Judith Green, the production director, tells you that the following assumptions were made when the budget was originally prepared:

- material is entirely a variable cost;
- light, heat and power is a semi-variable cost. The fixed element included in the budgeted figure was £40,000;
- production labour is a stepped cost. Each production employee can make up to 10,000 Deltas. Each production employee was budgeted to receive a basic wage of £12,000 per year with no overtime and no bonuses;
- there are no part-time employees;
- rent, rates and depreciation, and administrative expenses are fixed costs.

TASKS

1 (a) In preparation for the next Board meeting of Parkside Manufacturing Ltd, calculate the:

(i) budgeted cost of material per Delta;

(ii) budgeted variable cost per Delta of light, heat and power;

(iii) number of production employees assumed in the budget.

(b) Prepare a statement which compares the actual results of Parkside Manufacturing with the flexible budget, and identify any variances.

2 On receiving your flexible budget and variances, Judith Green tells you that:

- she does not understand why there is a need for the two types of budget, the one prepared by the previous management accountant and the flexible budget prepared by yourself;
- she does not know if it is necessary to investigate all variances;
- she is concerned that the original budgeted sales volume was so different from the actual sales volume and is considering the use of linear regression to improve sales forecasting of Deltas.

Judith Green asks you to write a brief report in preparation for the Board meeting. In your report you should:

(a) briefly explain the different purposes of the two types of budget, and explain which one should be used to compare with the actual results;

(b) suggest THREE general factors that need to be taken into account in deciding whether or not to investigate variances;

(c) briefly explain THREE limitations to the use of linear regression in sales forecasting.

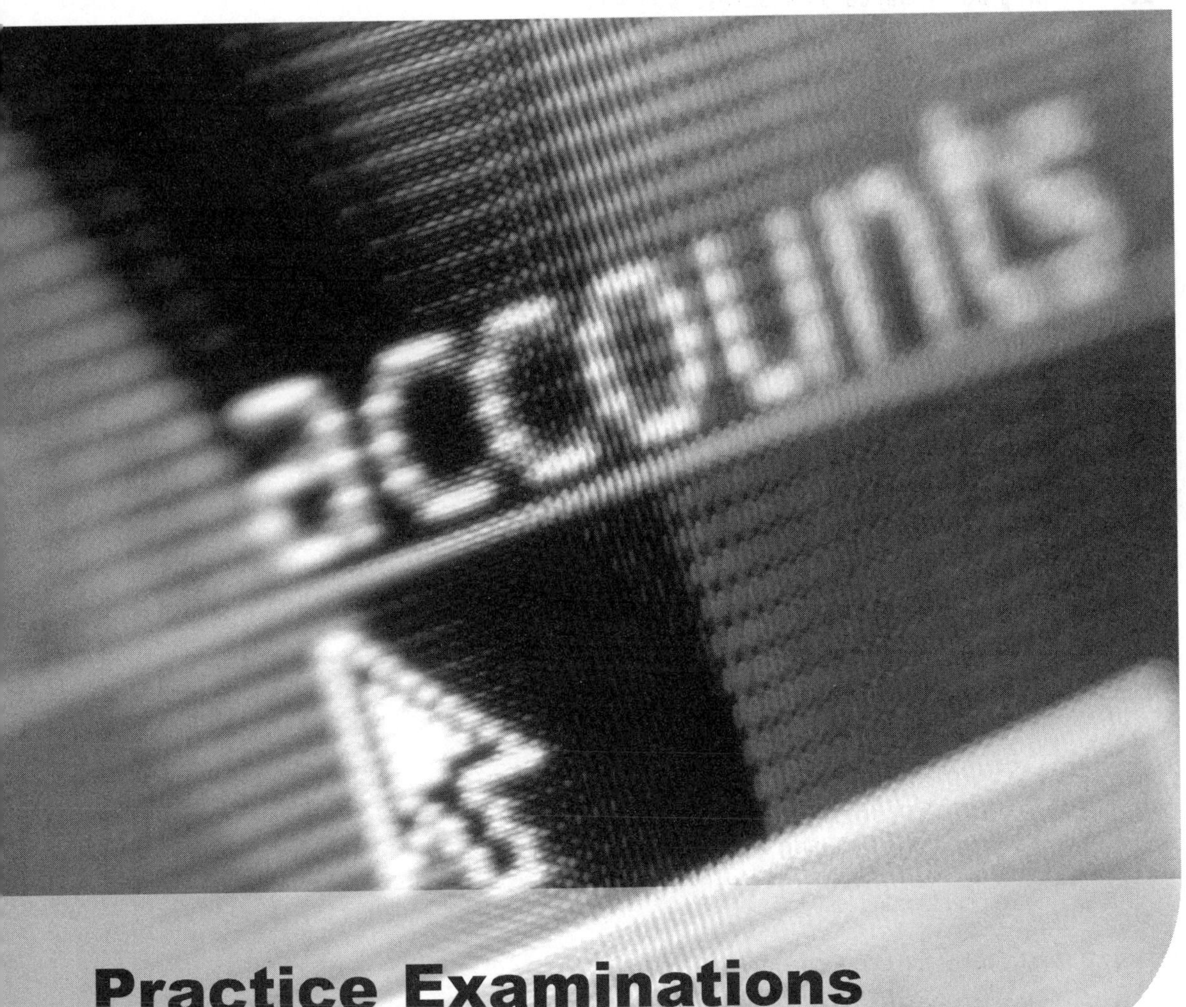

Practice Examinations

This section contains assessment tasks derived from past and specimen Examinations for Units 8 and 9, reproduced by kind permission of AAT.

Details of these practice examinations are set out on the next page.

PRACTICE EXAMINATIONS

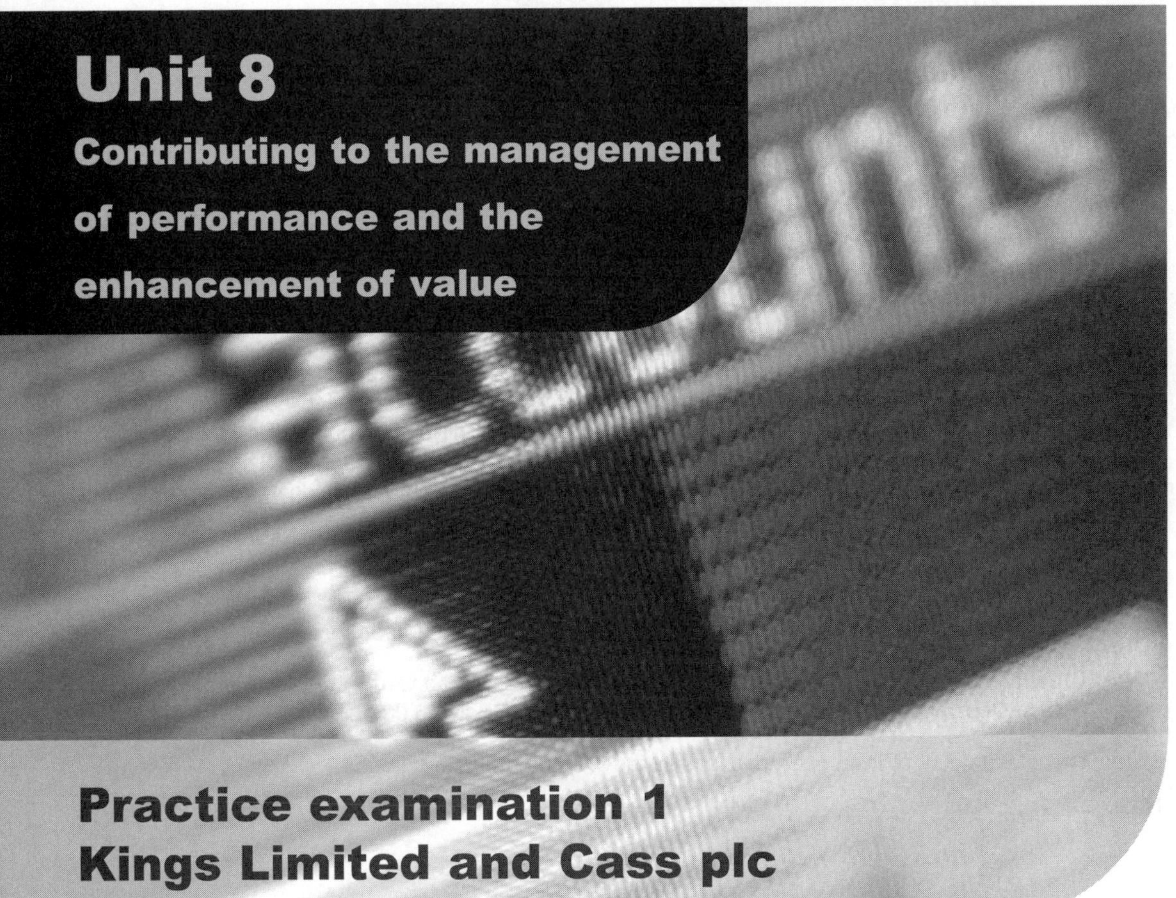

Unit 8

Contributing to the management of performance and the enhancement of value

Practice examination 1 Kings Limited and Cass plc

This practice examination is in two sections.

Time allowed: three hours plus a recommended fifteen minutes reading time.

You should spend about 90 minutes on each section.

You have to show competence in both sections, so attempt and aim to complete every task in both sections.

Include all essential workings with your answers.

SECTION 1: KINGS LTD

DATA

Kings Ltd manufactures several types of small machines. You are working as an assistant cost accountant in Kings Ltd and have been requested to carry out the following tasks.

Department D of Kings Ltd produces a single type of moulded and hand-finished component (code D1) for use by other departments of the company in the manufacture of its products. Kings Ltd uses standard costing in all its departments. Separate absorption rates are calculated for each department for fixed overheads, based on direct labour hours. The standard cost per unit of Component D1 includes 75g of direct material at £4.40 per kg and 30 minutes of direct labour time at £8.00 per hour. The planned direct labour hours for Department D are 15,000 per month. Kings Ltd has apportioned budgeted fixed overheads of £270,000 per month to Department D.

The actual results for Department D in the month of June 2003 were as follows:

- Direct material purchased and used cost a total of £8,400 at £4.20 per kg.
- The actual direct labour cost was £120,400 and the hours worked were sufficient to produce 28,000 units of Component D1, although production was actually only 25,000 units.
- The total amount of fixed overhead was in line with the budgeted amount.

Note: 1 kg = 1,000g.

Task 1.1

(a) Calculate the standard cost per unit of Component D1.

(b) Calculate for department D of Kings Ltd for the month of June 2003:

(i) the actual quantity of direct material used

(ii) the actual number of direct labour hours

(iii) the actual total amount of fixed overhead

(c) Calculate the following variances for department D of Kings Ltd for June 2003:

(i) direct material price variance

(ii) direct material usage variance

(iii) direct labour rate variance

(iv) direct labour efficiency variance

(v) fixed overhead expenditure variance

(vi) fixed overhead capacity variance

(vii) fixed overhead efficiency variance

(viii) fixed overhead volume variance

(d) Prepare a report for Ben Wray, the production manager for Department D, showing the following information:

   (i) the standard cost per unit of Component D1, as calculated in (a)

   (ii) a statement reconciling the total actual cost of the units of production of Component D1 in June 2003 with the total standard cost for that number of units, showing the variances calculated in (b)

   (iii) brief comments on the statement you have prepared, referring in particular to the meaning and usefulness to Ben Wray of the calculated fixed overhead variances

DATA

On receipt of the variance report, Ben Wray, who is a relatively new member of staff at Kings Ltd, replies as follows:

KINGS LTD

MEMORANDUM

To: Assistant Cost Accountant

From: B. Wray, Production Manager, Dept. D

Date: 17 July 2003

Subject: Variance Report for June 2003.

I have a number of queries about the variance report for June 2003. I have had a meeting with the Management Accountant, who is trying to improve the efficiency and usefulness of the reporting system. He suggested introducing control limits and using exception reporting. I am meeting him again next week and would like to use the June report as an example of the effects of these and also of the sort of problems I have. Could you clarify the following points for me:

1 Can variances be caused by errors, which would not necessarily be my responsibility?

2 It seems that some of these variances are outside my control, so would an alternative form of report be more useful? I really need information on which I can take action.

3 What difference would it make to the effectiveness of the reporting system if the Management Accountant's ideas of introducing control limits and using exception reporting were introduced?

4 Referring to June 2003 specifically, would the following factors have made a difference to the variances, and if so, which ones would be affected? Can you calculate the part of the variance which is due to these factors?

   - In June, several trainees joined the department and the experienced workers had to show them the working methods.
   - Due to the slow working caused by training the new workers, we fell behind with production at one point, and I had to agree 150 hours of exceptional overtime at time and a half in order to catch up. The cost of this all went into the direct labour total for the month.
   - The training resulted in wastage of about 60 kg of the direct material, due to work having to be rejected.

Task 1.2

Prepare a reply to Ben Wray's memorandum, showing the following information and referring to your answer to Task 1.1 where appropriate.

a) reply to question 1 in the Memorandum, including in your answer two examples of errors which may cause variances

b) reply to question 2 in the Memorandum, explaining what is meant by 'controllability' of costs and suggesting how its consideration could improve the form of the report

c) reply to question 3 in the Memorandum, explaining the terms 'control limits' and 'exception reporting' and the improvements that may be made using these ideas

d) reply to question 4 in the Memorandum, including in your answer an explanation of which variances would be affected by these factors, together with calculations where possible.

SECTION 2: CASS PLC – AMOS LTD AND BOYD LTD

DATA

You are employed as an assistant management accountant by Cass plc. Amos Ltd and Boyd Ltd are two companies owned by Cass plc. Both companies manufacture the same product, which is sold at £250 per unit to the agricultural industry. Amos Ltd and Boyd Ltd operate in similar geographical areas and both companies use the same accounting policies, including straight-line depreciation.

Financial and other information is given below for Amos Ltd and Boyd Ltd, followed by certain performance indicators which have been calculated for Boyd Ltd, for the year ended 31 March 2004.

Amos Ltd Operating Statement: year to 31 March 2004

Units produced and sold	14,000	
Number of employees	16	
	£000s	*£000s*
Turnover		3,500
Material and bought-in services	1,700	
Production labour	315	
Other production expenses	787	
Depreciation – buildings	24	
Depreciation – plant and machinery	100	
Administration and other expenses	154	3,080
Operating profit		420

Amos Ltd: Extract from Balance Sheet as at 31 March 2004

	£000s	£000s	£000s
Fixed assets	*Cost*	*Provision for Depreciation*	*NBV*
Buildings	1,200	480	720
Plant and Machinery	1,000	600	400
	2,200	1,080	1,120
Net current assets			
Stock	178		
Debtors	65		
Cash	12		
Creditors	(95)		160
			1,280

Boyd Ltd Operating Statement: year to 31 March 2004

Units produced and sold	24,000	
Number of employees	25	
	£000s	£000s
Turnover		6,000
Material and bought-in services	3,100	
Production labour	485	
Other production expenses	1,200	
Depreciation – buildings	40	
Depreciation – plant and machinery	150	
Administration and other expenses	245	5,220
Operating profit		780

Boyd Ltd: Extract from Balance Sheet as at 31 March 2004

	£000s	£000s	£000s
Fixed assets	*Cost*	*Provision for Depreciation*	*NBV*
Buildings	2,000	120	1,880
Plant and Machinery	1,500	450	1,050
	3,500	570	2,930
Net current assets			
Stock	260		
Debtors	95		
Cash	9		
Creditors	(154)		210
			3,140

Boyd Ltd: Performance indicators for the year to 31 March 2004

• Units produced per employee	960
• Production labour cost per unit	£20.21
• Added value per employee	£116,000
• Asset turnover	1.9 times
• Operating profit margin	13.0%
• Return on capital employed	24.8%
• Operating profit per employee	£31,200
• Units per £1,000 of NBV of Fixed Assets	8.2

Task 2.1

(a) Calculate the following performance indicators for Amos Ltd for the year ended 31 March 2004 and set them out in a table with those of Boyd Ltd for comparison:

(i) units produced per employee
(ii) production labour cost per unit
(iii) added value per employee
(iv) asset turnover
(v) operating profit margin
(vi) return on capital employed
(vii) operating profit per employee
(viii) units produced per £1,000 of Net Book Value of *fixed assets*

(b) The Managing Director of Boyd Ltd has claimed that his company outperforms Amos Ltd as it achieves a much higher level of productivity.

Explain briefly what is meant by productivity and whether the performance indicators shown in (a) above for the two companies support this claim.

DATA

The Chief Executive of Cass plc requires a summary of the performance of Amos Ltd and Boyd Ltd for the year ended 31 March 2004, emphasising in particular the efficiency of the two companies.

Task 2.2

Prepare a brief summary, to be attached to the comparative table of performance indicators, for submission to the Chief Executive of Cass plc. The summary should include the following:

(a) Explain your understanding of the term 'efficiency' when applied to a profit-making organisation.

(b) From the eight performance indicators used by Cass plc above, suggest **two** which could be used to measure efficiency and state whether they indicate that Amos Ltd or Boyd Ltd is more efficient.

(c) Explain briefly one reason why the indicators may show one company to be more efficient, but the other to have higher productivity.

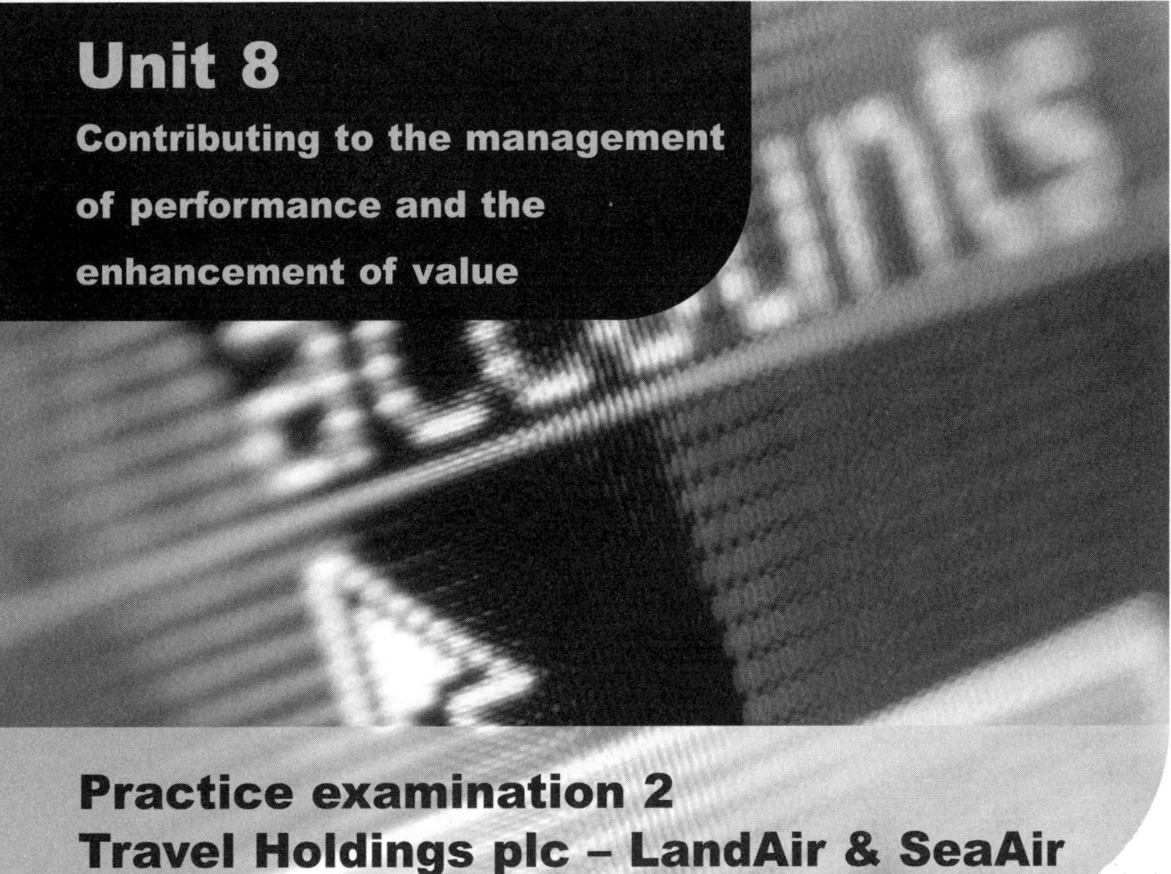

Unit 8

Contributing to the management of performance and the enhancement of value

Practice examination 2
Travel Holdings plc – LandAir & SeaAir

This practice examination is in two sections.

Time allowed: three hours plus a recommended fifteen minutes reading time.

You should spend about 90 minutes on each section.

You have to show competence in both sections, so attempt and aim to complete every task in both sections.

Include all essential workings with your answers.

SECTION 1: TRAVEL HOLDINGS PLC

DATA

You are employed as a management accountant in the head office of Travel Holdings plc. Travel Holdings owns a number of transport businesses. One of them is Travel Ferries Ltd. Travel Ferries operates ferries which carry passengers and vehicles across a large river. Each year, standard costs are used to develop the budget for Travel Ferries Ltd. The latest budgeted and actual operating results are given below.

Travel Ferries Ltd

Budgeted and actual operating results for the year to 30 November 2003

Operating data	*Budget*	*Budget*	*Actual*	*Actual*
Number of ferry crossings	6,480		5,760	
Operating hours of ferries	7,776		7,488	
Cost data		£		£
Fuel	1,244,160 litres	497,664	1,232,800 litres	567,088
Labour	93,312 hours	466,560	89,856 hours	471,744
Fixed overheads		466,560		472,440
Cost of operations		1,430,784		1,511,272

Other accounting information

- fuel and labour are variable costs
- fixed overheads are absorbed on the basis of budgeted **operating hours.**

Task 1.1

(a) Calculate the following information:

(i) the standard price of fuel per litre

(ii) the standard litres of fuel for 5,760 ferry crossings

(iii) the standard labour rate per hour

(iv) the standard labour hours for 5,760 ferry crossings

(v) the fixed overhead absorption rate per budgeted operating hour

(vi) the standard operating hours for 5,760 crossings

(vii) the standard fixed overhead cost absorbed by the actual 5,760 ferry crossings

(b) Using the data provided in the operating results and your answers to part (a), calculate the following variances:

  (i) the material price variance for the fuel
  (ii) the material usage variance for the fuel
  (iii) the labour rate variance
  (iv) the labour efficiency variance
  (v) the fixed overhead expenditure variance
  (vi) the fixed overhead volume variance
  (vii) the fixed overhead capacity variance
  (viii) the fixed overhead efficiency variance

(c) Prepare a statement reconciling the actual cost of operations to the standard cost of operations for the year to 30 November 2003.

DATA

On receiving your reconciliation statement, the Chief Executive is concerned about the large number of adverse variances. She is particularly concerned about the excessive cost of fuel used during the year. A colleague informs you that:

- the actual market price of fuel per litre during the year was 20% higher than the standard price
- fuel used varies directly with the number of operating hours
- the difference between the standard and actual operating hours for the 5,760 ferry crossings arose entirely because of adverse weather conditions

Task 1.2

Write a Memo to the Chief Executive. Your memo should include the following:

(a) subdivide the material price variance into:

  (i) the part arising from the standard price being different from the actual market price of fuel, and
  (ii) the part due to other reasons.

(b) (i) for the actual 5,760 crossings, calculate the number of additional operating hours which were caused by the adverse weather conditions

  (ii) for the material usage variance, calculate the part of the variance arising from the additional operating hours and the part due to other reasons

  (iii) for the labour efficiency variance, calculate the part arising from the additional operating hours and the part due to other reasons.

(c) Suggest and explain briefly **one** way in which the reporting of variances in Travel Ferries Ltd could be improved.

SECTION 2: LANDAIR AND SEAAIR

DATA

LandAir and SeaAir are two small airlines operating flights to Waltonville. LandAir operates from an airport based at a town on the same island as Waltonville but SeaAir operates from an airport based on another island. In both cases, the flight to Waltonville is 150 air-miles. Each airline owns a single aircraft, an 80-seat commuter jet, and both airlines operate flights for 360 days per year.

You are employed as the management accountant at SeaAir and report to Carol Jones, SeaAir's chief executive. Recently, both airlines agreed to share each other's financial and operating data as a way of improving efficiency. The data for the year to 31 May 2003 for both airlines is reproduced below, followed by the performance indicators for LandAir.

Operating Statement for the year ended 31 May 2003

	LandAir		**SeaAir**	
	$000	*$000*	*$000*	*$000*
Revenue		51,840		29,700
Fuel & aircraft maintenance	29,160		14,580	
Take-off & landing fees at Waltonville	4,320		2,160	
Aircraft parking at Waltonville	720		2,880	
Depreciation of aircraft	500		400	
Salaries of flight crew	380		380	
Home airport costs	15,464	50,544	8,112	28,512
Net Profit		1,296		1,188

Extract from Balance Sheet at 31 May 2003

	LandAir	SeaAir
	$000	*$000*
Fixed assets:		
Aircraft	10,000	10,000
Accumulated depreciation	2,500	4,000
Net book value	7,500	6,000
Net current assets	3,300	5,880
	10,800	11,880
Other operating data		
Number of seats on aircraft	80	80
Return flights per day	12	6
Return fare	$200	$275
Air-miles per return flight	300	300

Performance indicators for LandAir

Return on capital employed	12.00%
Asset turnover per year	4.80 times
Sales (or net profit) margin	2.50%
Actual number of return flights per year	4,320
Actual number of return passengers per year	259,200
Average seat occupancy (note 1)	75.00%
Actual number of passenger miles (note 2)	77,760,000
Cost per passenger mile	$0.65

Notes

1 Actual number of return passengers ÷ maximum possible number of return passengers on actual flights.

2 Actual number of passengers carried x number of miles flown.

Task 2.1

Carol Jones asks you to prepare the following performance indicators for SeaAir:

(a) return on capital employed

(b) asset turnover

(c) sales (or net profit) margin

(d) actual number of return flights per year

(e) actual number of return passengers per year

(f) average seat occupancy

(g) actual number of passenger-miles

(h) cost per passenger-mile.

DATA

On reviewing the performance indicators you have calculated for SeaAir and comparing them with those for LandAir, Carol Jones is concerned that SeaAir has a lower Return on Capital Employed, even though it has a higher Net Profit Margin. She reminds you that there is a link between the Return on Capital Employed, the Asset Turnover and the Net Profit Margin and asks you to prepare answers to the following questions in the next Task.

Task 2.2

(a) State the equation which links the Return on Capital Employed, the Asset Turnover and the Net Profit Margin. Using the equation, calculate the Asset Turnover which SeaAir would require in order to achieve the same Return on Capital employed as LandAir, assuming SeaAir's Net Profit margin was as calculated in Task 2.1 (c) above.

(b) Calculate the Revenue which SeaAir would have obtained in the year ended 31 May 2003, if the Asset Turnover had been at the level calculated in (a) above, in this task.

(c) Calculate the percentage increase in the number of passengers in the year ended 31 May 2003 which would have been necessary in order to obtain the Revenue calculated in (b) above.

(d) Assuming SeaAir had run the same number of flights, what would the average seat occupancy have been if the increase in the number of passengers calculated in (c) above had been achieved?

(e) Suggest **one** way in which the Asset Turnover and hence the Return on Capital Employed could have been improved by SeaAir in the year ended 31 May 2003, other than by increasing the number of passengers.

(f) Suggest **one** way in which SeaAir could have increased its Revenue in the year ended 31 May 2003 other than by improving the average seat occupancy on its flights.

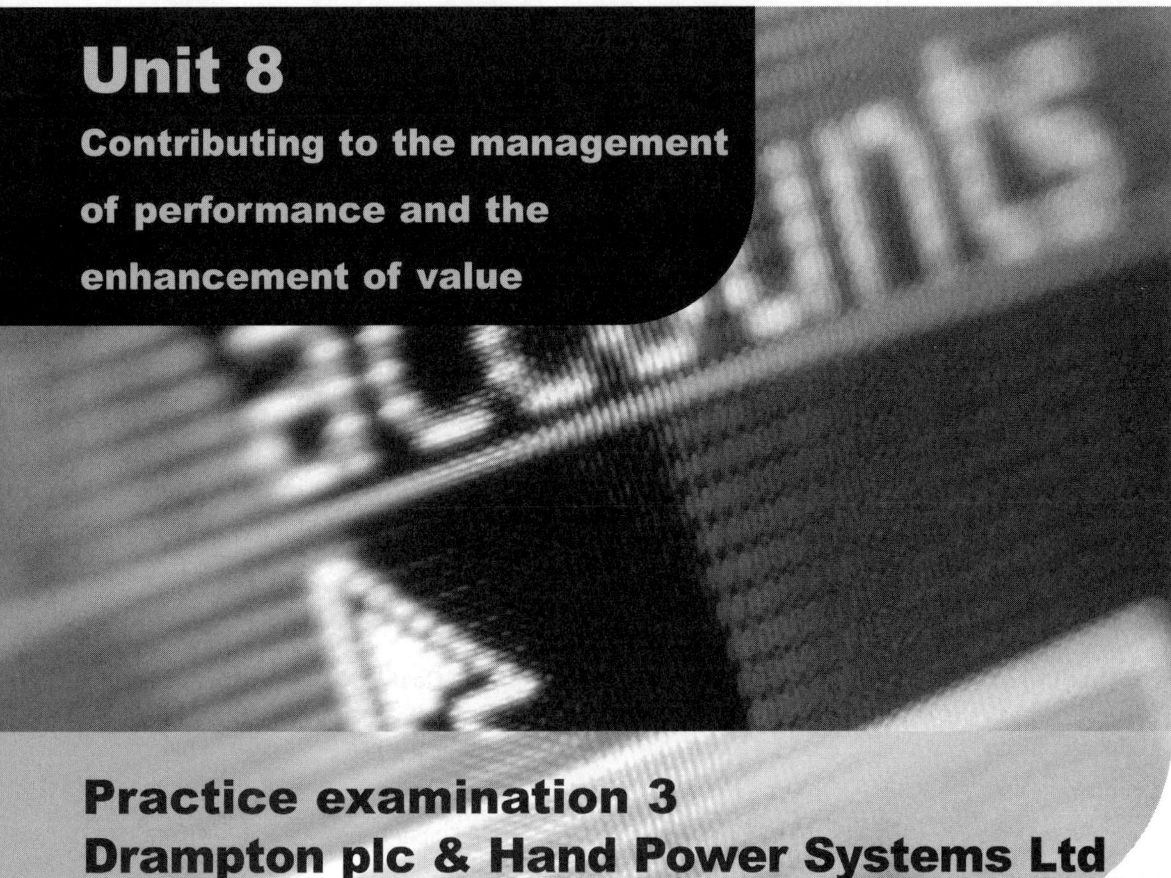

Unit 8
Contributing to the management of performance and the enhancement of value

Practice examination 3
Drampton plc & Hand Power Systems Ltd

This practice examination is in two sections.

Time allowed: three hours plus a recommended fifteen minutes reading time.

You should spend about 90 minutes on each section.

You have to show competence in both sections, so attempt and aim to complete every task in both sections.

Include all essential workings with your answers.

SECTION 1

DATA

You are employed as a financial analyst at Drampton plc, a computer retailer. One of your duties is to prepare a standard costing reconciliation statement for the finance director.

The company sells two types of computer, desktop computers for individual use and mainframe computers for large organisations. Desktop computers are sold by advertising in newspapers. Customers telephone Drampton to place an order and the telephone call is answered by trained operators. Drampton pays the cost of the telephone call. The total standard cost of one telephone call is shown below.

Standard cost of one call

Expense	**Quantity**	**Cost**	**Cost per call**
Telephone cost	1 unit	£0.07 per unit	£0.07
Operators' wages	6 minutes	£3.50 per hour	£0.35
Fixed overheads[1]	6 minutes	£6.50 per hour	£0.65
Standard cost of one telephone call			£1.07

[1] Fixed overheads are based on budgeted operator hours.

Drampton's finance director gives you the following information for the three months ended 31 May 2004.

	Quantity	*Cost*
• Budgeted number of calls		900,000 calls
• Actual number of calls		1,000,000 calls
• Actual expenses	*Quantity*	*Cost*
Telephone cost	1,200,000 units	£79,200
Operators' wages	114,000 hours	£478,800
Fixed overheads		£540,400
Actual cost of actual operations		£1,098,400

Task 1.1

(a) Calculate the following information:

(i) actual cost of a telephone unit

(ii) actual hourly wage rate of operators

(iii) standard number of operator hours for 1,000,000 calls

(iv) budgeted cost of fixed overheads for the 3 months ended 31 May 2004

(v) budgeted number of operator hours for the 3 months ended 31 May 2004

(vi) standard cost of actual operations

(b) Using the data given and your answers to part (a), calculate the following variances:

(i) price variance for telephone calls

(ii) usage variance for telephone calls

(iii) labour rate variance for the telephone operators

(iv) labour efficiency variance for the telephone operators

(v) fixed overhead expenditure variance

(vi) fixed overhead volume variance

(vii) fixed overhead capacity variance

(viii) fixed overhead efficiency variance

(c) Prepare a statement for the three months ended 31 May 2004 reconciling the standard cost of actual operations to the actual cost of actual operations.

DATA

Drampton plc has recently taken over Little Ltd, a small company making mainframe and desktop computers. Little appears to make all of its profits from mainframe computers. Drampton's finance director tells you that Little's fixed overheads are currently charged to production using standard labour hours and gives you their standard cost of making mainframe and desktop computers. These are shown below.

Little Ltd: Standard cost per computer

Model	**Mainframe**	**Desktop**
Annual budgeted volume	5	5,000
Unit standard cost	£	£
Material and labour	50,000	500
Fixed overhead	4,000	40
Standard cost per computer	54,000	540

The finance director asks for your help and suggests you reclassify the fixed overheads between the two models using activity based costing. You are given the following information.

- **Budgeted total annual fixed overheads**

	£
Set up costs	10,000
Rent and power – production area	120,000
Rent – stores area	50,000
Salaries of store issue staff	40,000
Total	220,000

- Every time Little makes a mainframe computer, it has to stop making desktop computers and rearrange the factory layout. The cost of this is shown as set-up costs. If the company did not make any mainframe computers, these costs would be eliminated.

- **Cost drivers**

	Mainframe	*Desktop*	*Total*
Number of set ups	5	0	5
Number of weeks of production	10	40	50
Floor area of stores (square metres)	400	400	800
Number of issues of stock	2,000	8,000	10,000

Task 1.2

Prepare a note for Drampton's finance director. In the note, you should use the cost drivers to:

(a) reallocate Little's budgeted total fixed annual overheads between mainframe and desktop production;

(b) show the revised *unit* fixed overheads for each of the two types of computers.

SECTION 2

DATA

Drampton plc is considering purchasing Hand Power Systems Ltd. Hand Power Systems makes a hand-held computer and has provided Drampton with its latest operating statement and balance sheet. These are shown below together with details of the orders received during the year and information about the sales returns.

Hand Power Systems Ltd: Operating statement for the year ended 31 May 2004

	Volume	*£000*	*£000*
Gross sales	21,000		6,300
Less sales returns	1,000		300
Turnover	20,000		6,000
Material		3,360	
Labour		960	
Production fixed overheads		480	
Cost of production	24,000	4,800	
Add opening finished stock	1,000	300	
Less closing finished stock	(5,000)	(1,350)	
Cost of sales	20,000		3,750
Gross profit			2,250
Research and development		768	
Training		576	
Customer support		240	
Marketing		200	
Administration		226	2,010
Net operating profit			240

Extract from Balance sheet at 31 May 2004

	£000	*£000*
Fixed assets		
Machinery & equipment:		
Cost		5,000
Accumulated depreciation		4,000
Net book value		1,000
Net current assets		
Stock of finished goods	1,350	
Debtors	1,500	
Cash	(426)	
Creditors	(424)	2,000
Net assets		3,000

Additional information

- Orders for 26,000 hand-held computers were received during the year ended 31 May 2004.
- Sales returns represent hand-held computers found to be faulty by customers. Customers had these replaced by fault-free computers.

Task 2.1

Prepare the following performance indicators for Hand Power Systems Ltd, for Drampton's finance director:

(a) gross profit margin

(b) net profit (or sales) margin

(c) return on capital employed

(d) asset turnover

(e) average age of debtors in months

(f) research and development as a percentage of the cost of production

(g) training as a percentage of the cost of production

(h) customer support as a percentage of turnover

(i) returns as a percentage of turnover

(j) average delay in months between placing an order and receiving a fault-free, hand-held computer

DATA

The finance director believes that a balanced scorecard will help in the analysis of Hand Power Systems performance and gives you the following information.

The balanced scorecard views performance measurement from four perspectives:

- the financial perspective: this is concerned with satisfying shareholders and measures used include the return on capital employed
- the customer perspective: this attempts to measure how customers view the organisation and is concerned with measuring customer satisfaction – examples include the speed of delivery and customer loyalty
- the internal perspective: this measures the quality of the organisation's output in terms of technical excellence and consumer needs – examples include unit cost and total quality measurement
- the innovation and learning perspective: this emphasises the need for continual improvement of existing products and developing new products to meet customers' changing needs; in a 'for profit' organisation, this might be measured by the percentage of turnover attributable to new products

Task 2.2

Name one balanced scorecard perspective being measured for each of the performance indicators in Task 2.1.

DATA

The finance director gives you the following additional information relating to Hand Power Systems for the year to 31 May 2005.

Accounting policies

- Stocks: the closing stock of finished goods is valued on a last-in, first-out basis and material prices have been falling throughout the year ended 31 May 2004.
- There are no raw material or work in progress stocks at any time.
- Depreciation: this is calculated on a straight-line basis assuming no residual value.

  The depreciation charge for the year was £1,000,000.

  Similar fixed assets in other companies have an average life of 10 years.

Other information

- Indices for this year and next year

	Selling prices	*Material costs*	*Sales volume*
Index year ended 31 May 2004	120	175	100
Forecast index year ended 31 May 2005	100	140	130

- Total quality management will be introduced. As a result, there will no longer be any sales returns.
- The hand-held computers will be made to order and so there will be no closing stocks.
- As a result of this year's research and development, new machinery and equipment will be introduced from 1st June 2004. This will result in a 25% saving in the labour cost per hand-held computer.
- The new machinery and equipment will also result in savings of £160,000 in the production fixed overheads.

Task 2.3

Write a memo to the finance director. In your memo you should:

(a) briefly state and explain the effect of the following accounting policies on Hand Power Systems' profit for the year ended 31 May 2004:

   (i) Stock valuation

   (ii) Depreciation

(b) calculate the following *forecast* data for the year ending 31 May 2005:

   (i) selling price per hand-held computer

   (ii) sales volume

   (iii) sales turnover

   (iv) material per hand-held computer

   (v) labour cost per hand-held computer

   (vi) production volume

   (vii) cost of production

   (viii) cost of sales

   (ix) gross profit

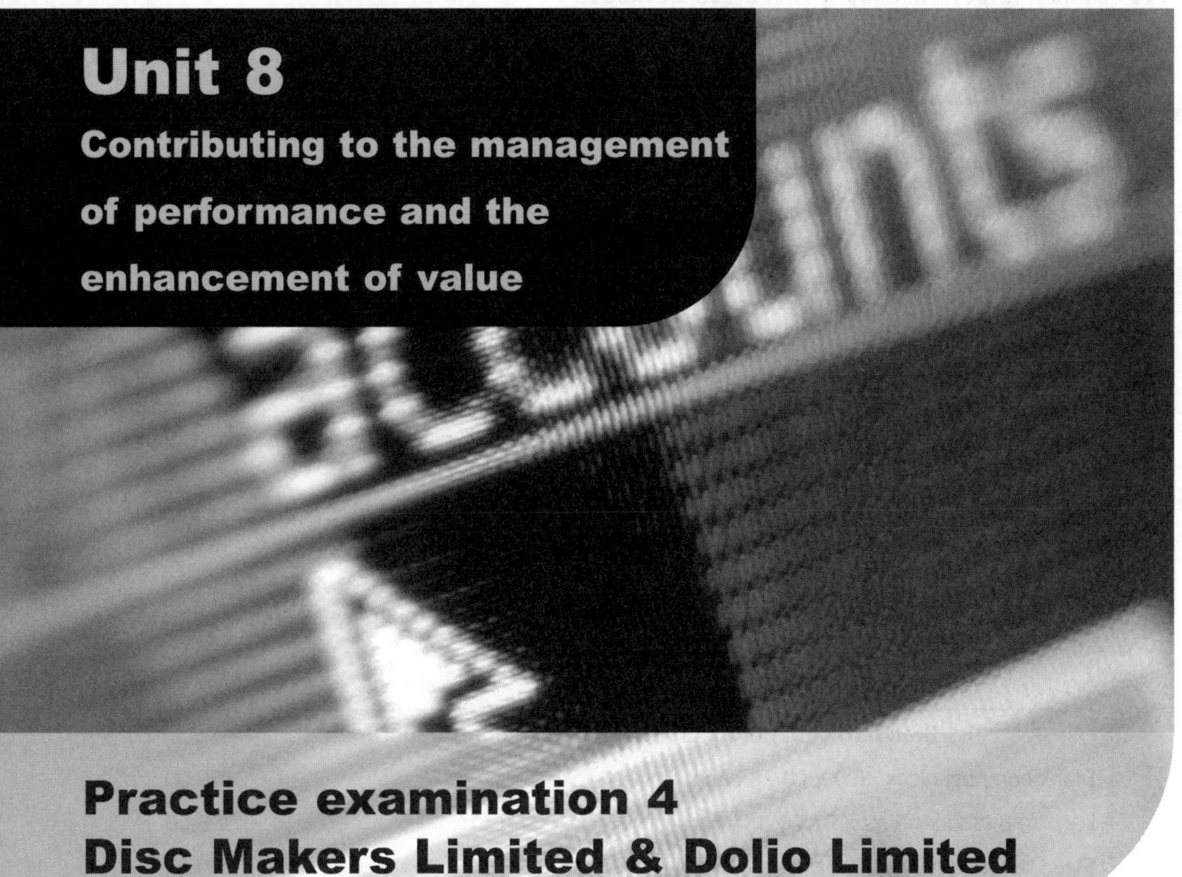

Unit 8

Contributing to the management of performance and the enhancement of value

Practice examination 4
Disc Makers Limited & Dolio Limited

This practice examination is in two sections.

Time allowed: three hours plus a recommended fifteen minutes reading time.

You are recommended to spend about 100 minutes answering Section 1 and 80 minutes answering Section 2.

You have to show competence in both sections, so attempt and aim to complete every task in both sections.

Include all essential workings with your answers.

SECTION 1

You should spend about 100 minutes on this section.

DATA

You are employed as the assistant management accountant at Disc Makers Ltd where you report to Jennifer Oldham, the managing director. The company makes compact discs for customers in other companies at its factory.

The factory has two departments that share the factory's fixed costs. The pressing department uses expensive machinery to write digital data from a master disc onto blank discs. The second department, the finishing department, then prints information on the front of the pressed discs, packages them and sends the completed discs to the customers.

Disc Makers uses standard costing in both departments. The standard costs for the pressing department are based on machine hours and planned production is 800 compact discs per machine hour. Each standard machine hour requires eight standard labour hours.

The standard costs for the pressing department, together with other data for the week ended 14 November 2003, are shown below.

Standard cost per machine hour – Pressing Department	
Blank compact discs: 800 x £0.20 each	£160.00
Labour: 8 labour hours x £7.00	£56.00
Fixed overheads	£200.00
Standard cost of pressing 800 compact discs per machine hour	£416.00

Pressing Department information:

- Actual cost of blank compact discs issued to production — £20,790
- Actual price paid for each blank compact disc — £0.21
- Actual number of *fault-free* pressed compact discs produced — 96,000 CDs
- Budgeted labour hours — 880 hours
- Actual labour hours worked — 980 hours
- Actual cost of labour — £7,252

Factory information:

- Budgeted *total* factory fixed costs — £33,000
- Budgeted *total* factory labour hours — 1,320 hours
- Actual *total* factory fixed costs — £34,500
- Both budgeted ***and*** actual fixed overheads are apportioned between the pressing and finishing departments on the basis of ***budgeted labour hours***.

Task 1.1

(a) Calculate the following information for the Pressing Department for the week ended 14 November 2003:

- (i) actual number of blank compact discs issued to production;
- (ii) budgeted machine hours of the department;
- (iii) standard number of compact discs produced per labour hour;
- (iv) standard labour hours produced;
- (v) budgeted fixed overheads of the pressing department;
- (vi) actual fixed overheads of the pressing department;
- (vii) standard fixed overhead rate per labour hour;
- (viii) actual cost of actual production, including fixed overheads;
- (ix) standard cost of actual production, including fixed overheads.

(b) Calculate the following variances for the Pressing Department:

- (i) material price variance;
- (ii) material usage variance;
- (iii) labour rate variance;
- (iv) labour efficiency variance;
- (v) fixed overhead expenditure variance;
- (vi) fixed overhead volume variance;
- (vii) fixed overhead capacity variance;
- (viii) fixed overhead efficiency variance.

(c) Prepare a statement reconciling the standard absorption cost of actual production to the actual absorption cost of actual production.

DATA

After reading your reconciliation statement, Jennifer Oldham tells you:

- She is not certain if all variances should be investigated. She explains that for every 100 **fault-free** compact discs produced in the week ended 14 November 2003, 2 had to be scrapped because they were faulty. As the unit cost of a blank CD is so small, she feels it is not worth investigating the other reasons for the material usage variance.
- The standard costs are also used for quoting prices to potential customers. When the standard costs were developed, Disc Makers assumed that customers would want their discs to be both pressed and finished. The demand for disc pressing is so high that it exceeds the capacity of the CD pressing department but most customers then take the pressed compact discs elsewhere for finishing.
- The pressing department requires a dust free, air conditioned environment using an expensive machine but the finishing department does not use any expensive resources.

Jennifer Oldham gives you an analysis of the budgeted factory fixed overheads showing their usage by department. This is reproduced below.

	Pressing	***Finishing***	***Total***
Rent, rates and insurance	£8,600	£1,300	£9,900
Air conditioning, heat, light and power	£9,600	£900	£10,500
Depreciation and maintenance	£12,600		£12,600
	£30,800	£2,200	£33,000

Task 1.2

Write a memo to Jennifer Oldham. In your memo you should:

(a) identify **four** issues to consider before deciding to investigate a variance;

(b) subdivide the material usage variance into that part due to discs being scrapped because they were faulty and that part due to other reasons;

(c) briefly explain, with reasons, why the use of budgeted labour hours to apportion fixed overheads between departments might cause the excess demand for the pressing department and the reduced demand for the finishing department.

SECTION 2

You should spend about 80 minutes on this section.

DATA

Dolio Ltd makes a single product, the Uno. The Uno is sold directly to domestic customers and Dolio is able to sell as many Unos as it can produce. Each Uno requires one X24, a specialist part which is in short supply.

The internal accounts of Dolio for the year to 30 November 2003, together with other data, are shown below.

Operating statement for the year ended 30 November 2003

	Units	£	£
Turnover			6,480,000
Purchases X24	12,000	1,200,000	
Less returns	1,200	120,000	
Net purchases	10,800	1,080,000	
Add opening stocks	1,200	120,000	
Less closing stocks	(1,200)	(120,000)	
X24 issued to production	10,800	1,080,000	
Other material and bought in services		108,000	
Production wages		1,296,000	
Variable cost of production and sales			2,484,000
Contribution			3,996,000
Production overhead		3,024,000	
Inspection cost of X24 goods received		69,600	
Cost of X24 returns		48,000	
Cost of remedial work		120,000	
Customer support for faulty products		194,400	
Administrative and distribution expenses		216,000	
Total fixed overheads			3,672,000
Net operating profit			324,000

BALANCE SHEET AT 30 NOVEMBER 2003

	£	£
Net fixed assets		1,600,000
Stock	120,000	
Cash	80,000	
Creditors	(180,000)	
Net current assets		20,000
Net assets		1,620,000
Financed by		£
Shareholders' funds		800,000
Loans		820,000
		1,620,000

OTHER DATA

- Number of production employees 140
- Maximum production capacity per year 12,000
- Dolio operates a Just-in-Time stock policy for the other material and bought in services but not for the X24.
- Closing stock only consists of units of X24.
- Creditors only arise from purchases of X24.
- Dolio does not offer credit facilities to customers or hold any stock of Unos.

You are employed by Dolio as its management accountant. One of your duties is to prepare management accounting information for Lewis Green, the Managing Director of Dolio.

Task 2.1

Lewis Green asks you to prepare the following performance indicators for Dolio:

(a) sales (or net profit) margin;

(b) return on capital employed;

(c) asset turnover;

(d) average age of stock in months;

(e) average age of creditors in months;

(f) added value per production employee;

(g) wages per production employee;

(h) capacity ratio (defined as actual production as a percentage of maximum production);

(i) contribution per Uno.

DATA

At a board meeting to consider the performance indicators, the Directors express concern about the *high cost of quality*. This is defined as the total of all costs incurred in preventing faults plus those costs involved in correcting faults once they have occurred. It is a single figure measuring all the explicit costs of quality – that is, those costs collected within the accounting system.

The Directors have also asked the supplier of the X24 to implement a Total Quality Management (TQM) programme to avoid faulty units of X24 being purchased and to also operate a Just-in-Time (JIT) policy to eliminate the need for Dolio to carry stocks.

Lewis Green tell you that:

- all costs making up the cost of quality are caused by the faulty units of X24;
- the supplier would agree to the TQM and JIT proposals but:
  - the cost per X24 would increase by £10;
  - supplies of the X24 would be limited to the 12,000 currently provided but each X24 would be guaranteed fault free;
  - supplies of the X24 would have to be paid for in the month received and no credit would be allowed;
- Dolio's cost of quality would be saved and stocks eliminated if the supplier implemented the TQM and JIT proposals;
- Dolio would want to keep its cash balance at £80,000;
- any surplus cash arising from the proposals would be used to reduce the £820,000 of loans.

Lewis Green is interested in knowing what the results of Dolio would have been if the TQM and JIT proposals had been applied to the results for the year ended 30 November 2003.

Task 2.2

Lewis Green asks you to calculate the following:

(a) cost of quality for Dolio Ltd;

(b) revised operating profit if the supplier's conditions were accepted;

(c) increase in cash balance before reducing the amount of the loans;

(d) revised capital employed if there were no stocks or creditors and if any surplus cash had been used to reduce the amount of the loans;

(e) revised return on capital employed.

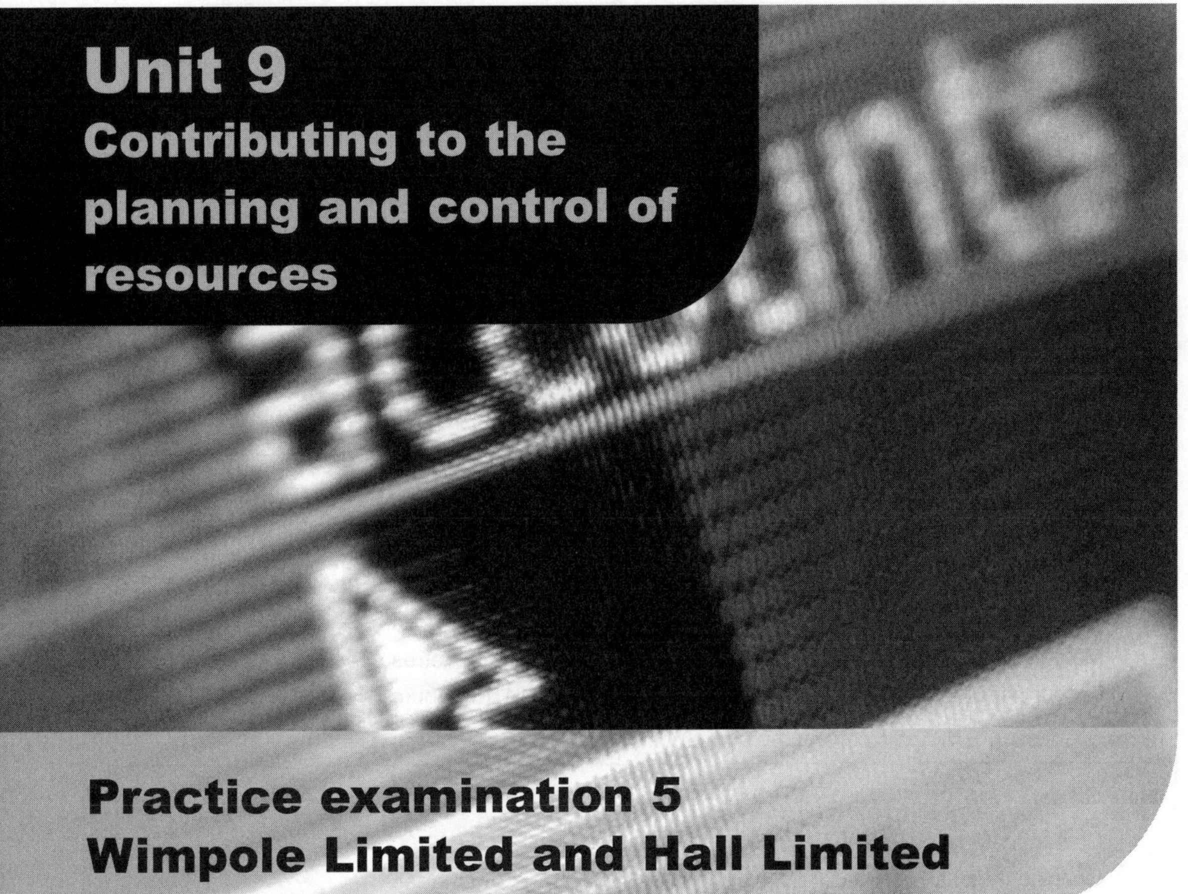

Unit 9
Contributing to the planning and control of resources

Practice examination 5
Wimpole Limited and Hall Limited

This practice examination is in two sections.

Time allowed: three hours plus a recommended fifteen minutes reading time.

You are recommended to spend about 70 minutes answering Section 1 and 110 minutes answering Section 2.

You have to show competence in both sections, so attempt and aim to complete every task in both sections.

Include all essential workings with your answers.

SECTION 1

DATA

You are employed as the assistant management accountant at Wimpole Ltd where one of your duties is the preparation of budgets every four weeks. You report to Ann Jones, the senior management accountant.

Wimpole Ltd makes several products, two of which are the Alpha and the Beta. Budget data for the two products for the four weeks ending 1 February 2004 is shown below.

Production and sales data	**Alpha**	**Beta**
Budgeted sales volume	2,000 units	3,000 units
Opening finished stocks	300 units	297 units
Closing finished stocks	500 units	595 units
Material per unit	10.00 metres	12.00 metres
Labour per unit	1.150 hours	1.380 hours

Note: production takes place evenly over the four weeks

Material data	
Cost of material per metre	£17.00
Opening material stock	8,750 metres
Closing material stock	15,530 metres
Wastage rate of material	3% of material issued to production

Labour data

46 employees work a guaranteed 35-hour week. The guaranteed wage for each employee is £210.00 per week. Any overtime necessary is paid at a rate of £8.00 per hour.

Since collecting the original budget data, you have discovered that:

- The maximum amount of material available from the supplier for the four weeks ending 1 February 2004 will be 61,580 metres.
- The wastage is material left over after lengths have been cut to make Alphas and Betas but before any labour cost has been incurred. The wastage has no scrap value.
- Betas are sold to a large furniture retailer under a long-term contract that cannot be broken. The budgeted sales volume of 3,000 Betas for the four weeks ending 1 February 2004 must be provided under the contract.
- It is not possible to reduce the level of any of the opening or closing stocks.

Task 1.1

Prepare the following information for Ann Jones for the four weeks ended 1 February 2004:

(a) the production budget in units for Alpha and Beta assuming there was no shortage of materials

(b) a statement taking into account the shortage of material and showing the:

  (i) metres of material available for production before any wastage

  (ii) metres of material required for Beta production (including any wastage)

  (iii) metres of material available for Alpha production

  (iv) number of Alphas to be produced

  (v) labour hours to be worked

  (vi) cost of labour budget

(c) the revised budgeted sales volumes for Alpha and Beta

DATA

Ann Jones is preparing the budgeted operating statement for a third product, the Delta, using a computer spreadsheet. Although she has entered selling price and cost data, these are uncertain and may be changed before the budget is agreed.

She asks you to complete the spreadsheet for the Delta using formulae that will allow a revised budgeted operating profit to be calculated automatically if price, cost and volume data change.

Task 1.2

Using the spreadsheet template below, enter formulas in cells B6 to B10 of the spreadsheet for:

(a) turnover

(b) total variable cost

(c) contribution

(d) fixed costs

(e) operating profit

	A	B
1	Selling price per unit	£140
2	Variable cost per unit	£70
3	Fixed costs per 4 week period	£40,000
4	Volume per period	1,000
5	4 weeks ending	1 February 2004
6	Turnover	
7	Total variable cost	
8	Contribution	
9	Fixed costs	
10	Operating profit	

SECTION 2

DATA

Wimpole Ltd also owns a subsidiary, Hall Ltd, which makes another product, the Omega. The budgeted and actual results for the year ended 30 November 2003 are shown below.

Hall Ltd: Budgeted and actual operating statement
Year ended 30 November 2003

	Budget	Actual
Sales volume (units)	*36,000*	*35,000*
	£	£
Turnover	1,440,000	1,365,000
Direct costs		
Material	432,000	500,000
Labour	216,000	232,000
Light, heat and power	92,000	96,000
Fixed overheads		
Depreciation	100,000	70,000
Other fixed overheads	400,000	420,000
Cost of production	1,240,000	1,318,000
Less closing stock	–	164,750
Cost of sales	1,240,000	1,153,250
Operating profit	200,000	211,750

Ann Jones tells you:

- material and labour are variable costs
- the budgeted total cost of light, heat and power includes a fixed element of £20,000
- the actual cost of light, heat and power includes a fixed element of £12,000
- there were no budgeted or actual opening stocks
- during the year, *actual* production was 40,000 Omegas, of which 5,000 were unsold at the year-end
- the closing stock of 5,000 Omegas were valued at their actual direct cost plus an appropriate proportion of fixed overheads
- the company did not purchase or sell any fixed assets during the year
- there was no work in progress at any time

Task 2.1

(a) Calculate the following:

(i) budgeted selling price per Omega

(ii) budgeted material cost per Omega

(iii) budgeted labour cost per Omega

(iv) budgeted variable cost of light, heat and power per Omega

(v) the percentage of cost of production carried forward in closing stock

(vi) total actual variable cost of sales by expenditure type

(vii) total actual fixed costs

(b) Prepare a flexible budget statement using variable (or marginal) costing, showing the budgeted and actual results and any variances.

DATA

The Chief Executive of Wimpole Ltd is Harry Easton. On receiving the original budgeted and actual operating statement, he has been very pleased with the performance of Hall Ltd. After reading your revised statement, however, he is concerned about the changes in both the budgeted profits and actual profits and is considering investigating whether or not the managers of Hall Ltd were responsible for the differences. Ann Jones suggests you write a memo to the Chief Executive.

Task 2.2

Write a short memo to Harry Easton, the Chief Executive. In your memo you should:

(a) briefly explain the main reason for:

(i) the difference between the original budget and the budget you prepared in task 2.1

(ii) the difference between the original operating profit and the operating profit you prepared in task 2.1

(b) give **two** possible reasons why the actual operating profit shown in task 2.1 was greater than the budgeted operating profit despite a lower sales volume

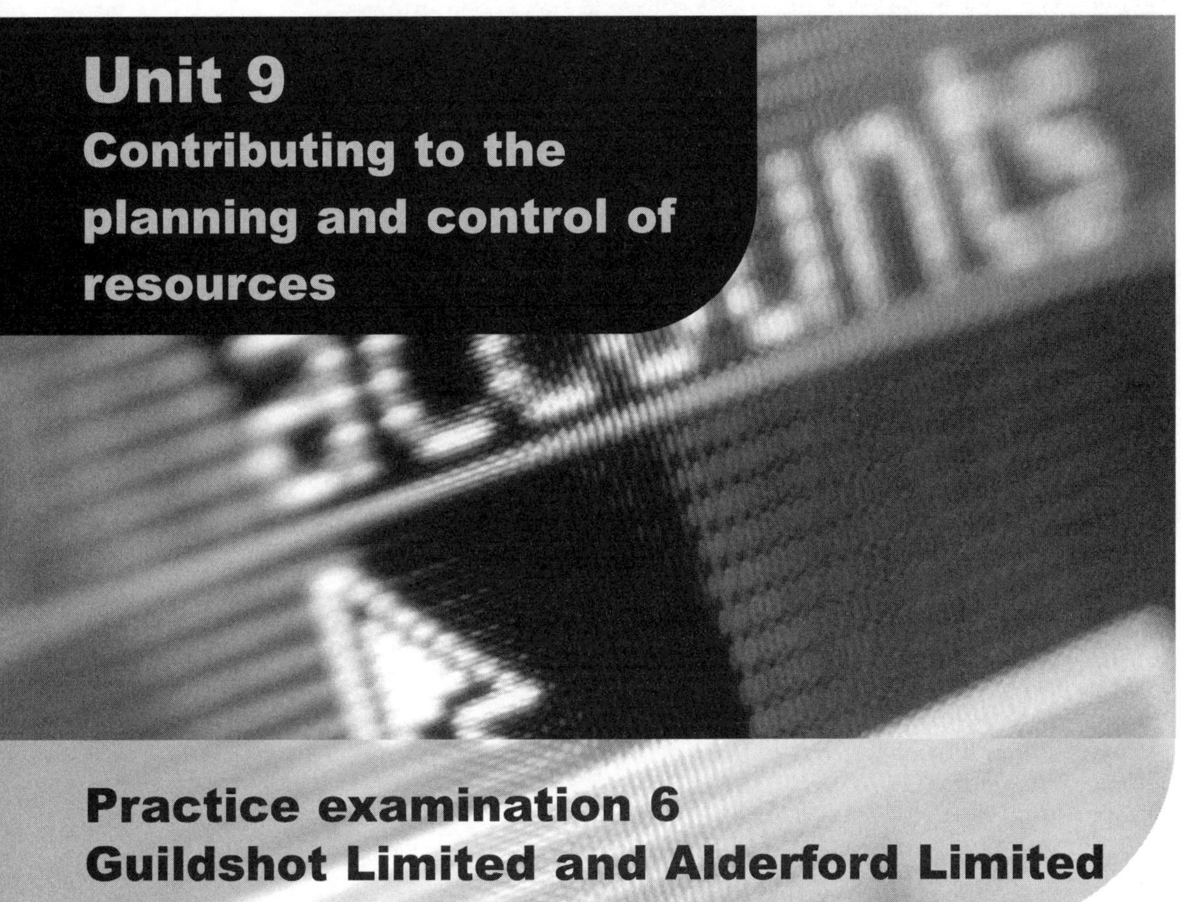

Unit 9
Contributing to the planning and control of resources

Practice examination 6
Guildshot Limited and Alderford Limited

This practice examination is in two sections.

Time allowed: three hours plus a recommended fifteen minutes reading time.

You are recommended to spend about 80 minutes answering Section 1 and 100 minutes answering Section 2.

You have to show competence in both sections, so attempt and aim to complete every task in both sections.

Include all essential workings with your answers.

SECTION 1

DATA

You are employed as an Accounting Technician by Guildshot Ltd, a company that makes statues. Statues are made in batches. A special powdered rock is added to water and poured into moulds. These moulds are then placed in ovens. Afterwards, the statues are removed from their moulds and inspected before being sold. At this inspection stage, some of the statues are found to be faulty and have to be destroyed. The faulty statues have no residual value.

Guildshot makes two types of statues, the Antelope and the Bear. Both use the same type of material and labour but in different amounts.

One of your duties is to prepare the production, material purchases and labour budgets for each four-week period. You are given the following information for period 8, the four-weeks ending 26 July 2004.

Forecast sales	**Antelope**	**Bear**
• Sales volume, period 8, four-weeks ending 26 July 2004	141,120 units	95,000 units
Product information	**Antelope**	**Bear**
• Opening finished stocks	30,576 units	25,175 units
• Kilograms of powdered rock per statue	0.75 kg	0.50 kg
• Production labour hours per statue	0.10 hours	0.05 hours
• Faulty production	2%	5%
Material information		
• Material: opening stock of powdered rock	30,000 kg	
• Material: closing stock of powdered rock	40,000 kg	
• Price per kilogram of powdered rock	£8.00	
Labour information		
• Number of production employees	140 employees	
• Days per week	5 days	
• Weeks per period	4 weeks	
• Hours per production employee per week	38 hours	
• Guaranteed weekly wage *	£228.00	

**The guaranteed weekly wage is paid even if hours produced are less than hours worked*

Closing finished stocks

The closing finished stocks are based on the forecast sales volume for period 9, the four-weeks ending 23 August 2004.

- Demand for the Antelope in period 9 is forecast to be 50% more than in period 8. The closing finished stock of Antelope statues for period 8 must be equal to 4 days' sales in period 9.
- Demand for the Bear in period 9 is forecast to be 30% more than in period 8. The closing finished stock of Bear statues for period 8 must be equal to 5 days' sales in period 9.

Other information

- The faulty production is only discovered after the statues have been made.
- For technical reasons, the company can only operate the ovens for five days per week.

Task 1.1

Prepare the following information for period 8, the four-weeks ending 26 July 2004:

(a) production budget in units for Antelopes and Bears;

(b) material purchases budget in kilograms;

(c) cost of the materials purchases budget;

(d) labour budget in hours;

(e) cost of the labour budget.

DATA

Hilary Green is the production director of Guildshot. She tells you that there are likely to be material and labour shortages in period 9. For commercial reasons, the company must fully meet the demand for Bear statues. As a result, it will not be able to meet all the demand for Antelope statues.

Hilary suggests it might be possible to meet the demand by producing extra Antelope statues in period 8. She gives you the following information:

- because of the technology involved, Guildshot cannot increase the number of production employees and the existing employees cannot work any overtime. The maximum hours are limited to the 38 hours per week for each production employee;
- it would be possible to buy up to a maximum 3,000 extra kilograms of powdered rock in period 8.

Task 1.2

(a) Calculate the maximum number of extra fault-free Antelope statues that could be made in period 8.

(b) Prepare a revised purchases budget in kilograms to include the production of the extra fault-free statues.

SECTION 2

DATA

Just over a year ago, Guildshot formed a subsidiary, Alderford Ltd, to make a new type of chemical. The chemical is sold in drums to the building industry where it is used to dry out new buildings.

You have been asked to help James Alexander, Alderford's managing director, prepare a report on the first twelve months of Alderford's operations.

James gives you a copy of the company's operating statement for the first twelve months of operations. This is shown below.

Alderford Ltd: Operating statement – 12 months ended 31 May 2004

	Budget	Actual
Number of drums produced and sold	80,000	125,000
	£000	£000
Turnover	2,400	4,000
Variable costs		
Material A	240	425
Material B	480	680
Material C	320	500
Semi-variable costs		
Power	270	440
Water	122	200
Stepped costs		
Supervisors	160	258
Fixed costs		
Rent and rates	250	250
Lighting and heating	120	118
Administrative expenses	200	240
Operating profit	238	889

James also tells you that:

- the budgeted fixed cost element of power was £110,000
- the budgeted fixed cost element of water was £90,000
- each supervisor can supervise the production of up to 10,000 drums of the chemical
- all other expenses are either totally fixed or vary directly with production and sales
- there are no opening or closing stocks of any sort

Task 2.1

(a) Calculate the budgeted variable cost per drum of the following inputs:

(i) material A

(ii) material B

(iii) material C

(iv) power

(v) water

(b) Prepare a statement showing Alderford's actual results, the flexible budget and any variances.

DATA

James Alexander is very pleased with the first year's results and wants the company to continue to improve. He hopes to increase sales while ensuring that budget holders keep costs under control.

He has three strategies for increasing the volume of sales:

- more sales to existing customers
- sales to new customers in the building industry
- the development of new markets

He is also considering whether sales and profits would improve if staff were motivated by performance related pay.

Task 2.2

Write a memo to James Alexander, in which you explain briefly:

(a) the meaning of 'controllable costs' for budget holders

(b) the best way of investigating and determining potential future sales in each of his three target markets

(c) the essential features of a performance related pay scheme for it to succeed in motivating staff.

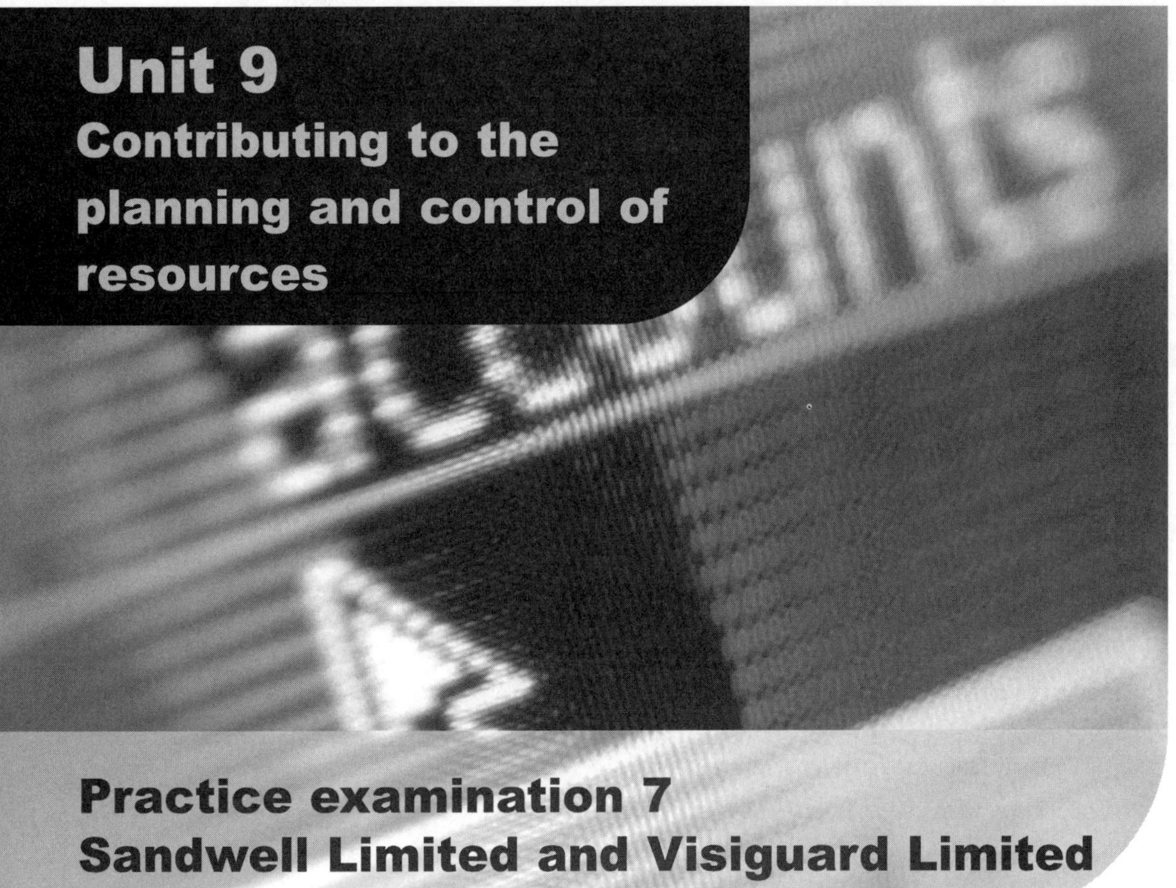

Unit 9

Contributing to the planning and control of resources

Practice examination 7
Sandwell Limited and Visiguard Limited

This practice examination is in two sections.

Time allowed: three hours plus a recommended fifteen minutes reading time.

You are recommended to spend about 80 minutes answering Section 1 and 100 minutes answering Section 2.

You have to show competence in both sections, so attempt and aim to complete every task in both sections.

Include all essential workings with your answers.

SECTION 1: SANDWELL LTD

DATA

Sandwell Ltd makes a single product, the Gamma. You are Sandwell's management accountant and you are responsible for preparing its operating budgets. The accounting year is divided into 13, four week periods. There are five days in each week.

The sales director of Sandwell has recently completed the following forecast sales volume for the next five periods.

Sales forecast five periods to 18 November 2003

Period number	1	2	3	4	5
Four weeks ending	29 Jul	26 Aug	23 Sep	21 Oct	18 Nov
Number of Gammas	19,400	21,340	23,280	22,310	22,310

The production director provides you with the following information:

- on completion of production, 3% of the Gammas are found to be faulty and have to be scrapped. The faulty Gammas have no scrap value;
- opening stocks: period 1, four weeks ending 29 July:
  - finished stock 3,880 Gammas;
  - raw materials 16,500 litres;
- closing stocks at the end of each period:
  - finished stock must equal 4 days' sales volume of Gammas in the next period;
  - raw materials must equal 5 days' gross production in the next period
- each Gamma requires 3 litres of material costing £8 per litre;
- each Gamma requires 0.5 hours of labour;
- Sandwell employs 70 production workers who each work a 40 hour week. Each employee is paid a guaranteed wage of £240 per week;
- the cost of any overtime is £9 per hour.

Task 1.1

Prepare the following budgets for the production director:

(a) gross production budget in Gammas (including faulty production) for each of the first four periods;

(b) material purchases budget in litres for each of the first three periods;

(c) cost of the material purchases for each of the first three periods;

(d) labour budget in hours for each of the first three periods including any overtime required in each period;

(e) cost of the labour budget for each of the first three periods, including the cost of any overtime.

DATA

After receiving your budgets, Sandwell's production director raises the following points:

- overtime payments should only be made if absolutely necessary;
- the faulty Gammas are thought to be caused by poor work practices by some of the production workers although this is not known for certain;
- the 70 production workers work independently of one another in making Gammas.

Task 1.2

Write a memo to the production director. In your memo, you should:

(a) explain and quantify the value of any possible overtime savings;

(b) suggest **one** extra cost which might be necessary to achieve the overtime savings;

(c) identify **two** advantages of sampling as a way of discovering reasons for the faulty Gammas;

(d) briefly explain the difference between true (or simple) random sampling, systematic sampling and stratified sampling;

(e) state which form of sampling Sandwell should use.

SECTION 2: VISIGUARD LTD

You should spend about 100 minutes on this section.

DATA

Visiguard Ltd is a division of Alton Products plc where you work as a management accountant. It makes a single product, the Raider. Just over a year ago, the chief executive of Alton Products, Mike Green, was concerned to find that Visiguard was budgeting to make only £20,000 profit in the year to 31 May 2003. As a result, he imposed his own budget on the division. His revised budget assumed:

- increased sales volume of the Raider;
- increased selling prices; and
- that suppliers would agree to reduce the cost of the material used in the Raider by 10%.

The only other changes to the original budget arose solely as a result of the increased volume in the revised budget.

The original budget and the revised budget imposed by Mike Green are reproduced below, together with the actual results for the year to 31 May 2003.

Visiguard Limited: Budgeted and actual operating statements for one year ended 31 May 2003

	Original budget	*Revised budget*	*Actual results*
Sales and production volume	10,000	11,000	11,600
	£	£	£
Turnover	1,400,000	1,760,000	1,844,400
Variable materials	400,000	396,000	440,800
Production and administrative labour	580,000	630,000	677,600
Light, heat and power	160,000	164,000	136,400
Fixed overheads	240,000	240,000	259,600
Budget profit	20,000	330,000	330,000

Task 2.1

Using the information provided in the two budgets, calculate the following:

(a) the unit selling price of the Raider in the revised budget;

(b) the material cost per Raider in the revised budget;

(c) the variable cost of the production and administrative labour per Raider;

(d) the fixed cost of production and administrative labour;

(e) the variable cost of light, heat and power per Raider;

(f) the fixed cost of light, heat and power.

DATA

On receiving the actual results for the year, Mike Green states that they prove that his revised budget motivated managers to produce better results.

Task 2.2

Write a memo to Mike Green. Your memo should:

(a) use the information calculated in Task 2.1 to prepare a flexible budget statement for Visiguard including any variances;

(b) identify **two** situations where an imposed budget might be preferable to one prepared with the participation of managers;

(c) briefly discuss whether or not his requirement that material costs be reduced would have motivated the managers of Visiguard;

(d) identify **two** ways in which profit could have increased without additional effort by the managers of Visiguard.

Unit 9
Contributing to the planning and control of resources

Practice examination 8
Berry Limited, Delta and Zeta

This practice examination is in two sections.

Time allowed: three hours plus a recommended fifteen minutes reading time.

You are recommended to spend about 100 minutes answering Section 1 and 80 minutes answering Section 2.

You have to show competence in both sections, so attempt and aim to complete every task in both sections.

Include all essential workings with your answers.

SECTION 1

DATA

Berry Ltd makes a product called the Delta. The only use for Deltas is as part of a machine made by World Products plc and World Products requires Berry to keep a minimum closing stock of Deltas.

You are the newly appointed management accountant employed by Berry Ltd and report to Nicola Brown, the managing director. She gives you the following information.

Accounting periods

- Both Berry Ltd and World Products plc divide the year into four week periods. Each week consists of five days and each day comprises eight hours.

Forecast demand for Deltas – first five periods of 2004

• Four weeks ending	30th January	27 February	26 March	23 April	21 May
	Period 1	Period 2	Period 3	Period 4	Period 5
Number of Deltas required	5,700	5,700	6,840	6,460	6,080

Finished Stocks and Work-in-progress

- World Products requires that closing stocks of Deltas at the end of *each* period must equal 3 days demand of the next period.
- The opening stock of Deltas for period 1, the four weeks ending 30 January 2004, will be 1,330 Deltas.
- There is no work in progress at any time.

Material

- Each Delta requires 6 litres of material.
- The material is currently supplied under a long term contract at a cost of £8.00 per litre and is made exclusively for Berry Ltd.
- The supplier of the material can only make a maximum of 34,000 litres in any four week period and Berry normally purchases the material in the same four week period it is used.
- Should Berry require more than 34,000 litres in a four week period, the supplier would be wiling to supply additional material in the preceding period, providing it had spare capacity.
- There is a readily available alternative source for the material but the cost is £12.00 per litre.
- Before buying from the alternative source, any shortage of material in a period should be overcome, where possible, by first purchasing extra material from the supplier in the **immediately preceding** period.

Labour

- There are 78 production employees who are paid a guaranteed basic wage of £160 per 40 hour week.

  Each Delta should take 2 labour hours to make but, due to temporary technical difficulties, the workforce is only able to operate at 95 per cent efficiency in periods 1 – 4.

  Any overtime incurred is payable at a rate of £6.00 per hour.

Task 1.1

Nicola Brown asks you to prepare the following budgets for **each** of the periods 1 – 4:

(a) the production budget in Deltas, using the 3 day stock levels required by World Products;

(b) the material purchases budget in litres;

(c) the cost of the material purchases;

(d) the labour budget in hours, including any overtime hours;

(e) the cost of the labour budget, including the cost of any overtime.

DATA

On receiving your budgets, Nicola Brown, the managing director, tells you that:

- she is concerned about the cost of the planned overtime and the extra cost of purchasing materials from the alternative source;
- the minimum demand in any four week period is forecast to be 5,700 Deltas;

She also believes that some immediate and longer term cost savings are possible if Delta stocks at the end of each period were sometimes less than the 3 days required by World Products.

Task 1.2

Write a memo to Nicola Brown. In your memo, you should:

(a) use the budget information prepared in task 1.1 to identify **one** immediate possible cost saving proposal other than reducing the 3 day stock requirement imposed by World Products;

(b) calculate the value of the cost savings in the proposal identified in part a);

(c) use the forecast of demand for Deltas to show whether or not:

(i) the need to obtain material supplies from the alternative supplier is a short term problem; and

(ii) the need for overtime payments is also a short term problem;

(d) suggest **two** cost savings which may be possible in the longer term.

SECTION 2

DATA

Just over twelve months ago, Berry Ltd started selling a new product, the Zeta, that no one else can make or sell. A budget was prepared at the time but this was then amended to take account of revised forecasts. The original and amended budgets, and the actual results for the year to 30 November 2003, are shown below in an operating statement prepared by the previous management accountant.

Zeta: Budgeted and actual operating results for the year to 30 November 2003

	Original budget		**Amended budget**		**Actual results**	
	Units	£000	*Units*	£000	*Units*	£000
Turnover	20,000	700	22,000	770	23,000	782
Material		160		176		225
Labour		300		330		350
Production overhead		74		74		75
Cost of production	20,000	534	22,000	580	25,000	650
less closing stock	nil	nil	nil	nil	2,000	52
Cost of sales	20,000	534	22,000	580	23,000	598
Gross profit		166		190		184
General expenses		110		114		125
Operating profit		56		76		59

Nicola Brown, the managing director of Berry Ltd, tells you that:

- the only change in costs and revenues between the two budgets arose from the forecast change in volume;
- material and labour are variable (or marginal) costs, production overhead is a fixed cost and general expenses is a semi fixed cost;
- both budgets assumed there would be no opening and no closing stocks.

She also gives you the following information about the actual results:

- the actual results have been prepared using absorption costing;
- the closing stock valuation includes a proportion of production overhead;
- general expenses include £71,000 which do not vary with changes in either sales or production volumes;
- the balance of general expenses are selling expenses and vary with Zetas sold;
- the actual unit cost of material and labour has remained the same throughout the year.

Nicola Brown is concerned that the actual profit for the year is less than the revised budgeted profit. She asks you to prepare an analysis showing why the two profit figures are different.

Task 2.1

Prepare an analysis for Nicola Brown. In your analysis you should:

(a) calculate the following **budgeted** data:

(i) selling price per Zeta;

(ii) material cost per Zeta;

(iii) labour cost per Zeta;

(iv) variable (or marginal) cost of general expenses per Zeta;

(v) fixed cost of general expenses;

(b) identify the **actual** production fixed costs incurred during the year;

(c) redraft the **actual** results for the year on a marginal costing basis;

(d) prepare a variable (or marginal) costing flexible budget statement for the year to 30 November 2003 showing:

(i) the actual results on a marginal costing basis;

(ii) the appropriate flexible budget; and

(iii) any variances.

DATA

After receiving your statement comparing the actual marginal costing results with the flexible budget, Nicola Brown tells you that:

- she does not understand why the budget in your statement is different from the agreed revised budget nor why some costs have changed but others have remained the same;
- she does not understand why the actual results in your statement are different from the actual results in the operating statement prepared by the previous management accountant;
- she is concerned that the actual sales volume was significantly different from the budgeted sales volume.

Task 2.2

Write a memo to Nicola Brown. In your memo you should *briefly*:

(a) give **one** reason why the budget in your statement answering task 2.1(d) is different from the revised budget;

(b) explain why the actual results in your statement are different from the actual results given in the task data;

(c) explain **three** forecasting techniques Berry Ltd can currently use to estimate the demand for Zetas;

(d) explain **one** forecasting technique that Berry Ltd is currently unable to use to estimate the demand for Zetas.